THE BEST WINES IN THE SUPERMARKETS 2018

NED HALLEY

foulsham
LONDON • NEW YORK • TORONTO • SYDNEY

W. Foulsham & Co. Ltd
for Foulsham Publishing Ltd
The Old Barrel Store, Drayman's Lane, Marlow, Bucks SL7 2FF

Foulsham books can be found in all good bookshops and direct from www.foulsham.com

ISBN: 978-0-572-04692-7

Text copyright © 2017 Ned Halley
Series, format and layout design © Foulsham Publishing Ltd

Cover photographs © Thinkstock

A CIP record for this book is available from the British Library

The moral right of the author has been asserted

Printed and bound in Great Britain by Martins the Printers Ltd

Contents

—A matter of choice—

How do you choose your supermarket? I suspect location was once the decisive factor. But now that the geography of grocery retailing causes rivals to cluster together in city centres, retail parks and country towns, more complex criteria come into play.

The present oversupply of multiple outlets is to be blamed, I suppose, on those relative newcomers, the German discounters. Aldi, heading for 1,000 UK stores by 2022, and Lidl, accelerating in pursuit (did you know Lidl already has 1,500 stores in France?) seem to pop up wherever there is a big indigenous supermarket close by.

It's not as if the retail map isn't already overcrowded. But never mind. We are spoiled for choice, and competition keeps prices keen. And while supermarkets used to be content to sell little other than branded goods, competing far more on price than diversity, own-label or 'exclusive' ranges have now become their most essential Unique Selling Point.

Nowhere is this more obvious than on the wine shelves. Sure, global brands like Blossom Hill and Gallo still occupy their paid-for spaces in some (though by no means all) of the major retailers, but savvy wine shoppers know where the best quality and value are to be found. The wines to which the supermarkets put their own names are your starting point.

And that, of course, is where *The Best Wines in the Supermarket*s comes in. More than 400 of the 500 wines reviewed in this edition are exclusive to the retailer under whose heading they appear. That's a lot of diversity, a lot of choice.

It might just signify, I like to think, that some of us are choosing our supermarket according to our wine preferences. Clearly the supermarkets themselves think this way because they are forever staging promotions – often expensively advertised online and in the wider media – offering hefty discounts, usually 25 per cent, on their entire ranges if you come in and buy at least six bottles.

Wine is becoming a promotional instrument in the widest sense. No other commodity is as frequently used to lure customers into supermarkets. The people who work in the wine departments of the giants hate having their carefully sourced and nurtured products slashed arbitrarily in price, possibly as loss-leaders. In between the periods of promotions, it becomes harder and harder to sell the wines at their full, often perfectly rational prices.

I do feel for the hard-working buyers, some of whom complain bitterly, albeit strictly off the record, about the promotion culture. But as customers of the supermarkets, the rest of us need to take full advantage.

This is still a good time to buy wine in supermarkets. There is quality and diversity in depth. Prices, in spite of Brexit and the wobbly pound, are remarkably steady. Even the effect of the outrageously punitive Budget of 2017, which left beer and spirit taxes unchanged but raised the excise duty on a 75cl bottle of still wine by 8p to £2.16 (fizz was up 10p to £2.77), seems to have been absorbed. Do note, though, that this tax, with VAT on it, now accounts for more than half of the value of a bottle of wine priced at £5.

And the £5 bottle of wine is by no means extinct. Well it wouldn't be, when you take into account that the average price paid retail per standard 75cl in Britain is currently just £5.39. Genuinely good wine at this price level is certainly getting harder to find, but for the guide this year I have picked out more than 80 individual items priced at under £6.

But it's a truism, of course, that you get more interesting wine if you're prepared to pay more. As the trade never tires of pointing out, the actual cash earned by the wine producer for a £5 bottle is something like 37p, while for a £10 bottle the sum is reckoned to be £2.76. Double your budget and you get seven to eight times the value in wine.

With a budget approaching a tenner or even above, the world of wine is wide open to you. And the supermarkets make a happy hunting ground. They might have lately reduced the overall numbers in their ranges, but in the mid-price zone the choice seems to me as varied as ever. European wines, in spite of the recent divorce unpleasantness, are in profusion. With 55 per cent of UK wine imports now from the EU, we can put cynically confected Australian, Californian and South African garbage behind us.

A whiff of scandal

Have I uncovered a scandal? Supermarkets appear to be ignoring Department of Health guidelines on 'safe' levels of drinking. In January 2016, the Chief Medical Officer, Dame Sally Davies, announced that there is no safe limit, but to minimize the risk of cancer and of diseases of the liver, no one should consume more than 14 units of alcohol per week, or 2 units – equivalent to one 150ml glass of wine – daily.

The wine trade has since had plenty of time to adjust its on-label recommendations to consumers accordingly. But I have yet to detect any such alteration made by a supermarket. All the labels I have checked continue to quote 'UK Government' advice that women should not exceed two to three units daily and men three to four units, based on the weekly recommendations of 21 and 28 units prevailing until Dame Sally's 2016 revision.

At the time this revision was made known there was controversy over the composition of the official committees responsible, their motives and qualifications. The new Alcohol Guidelines came into force on 8 January 2016, but their content was subsequently put out for consultation in the Dept of Health's own words, to 'seek the public's view on how helpful and easy to use the new advice is, not the scientific basis for it'.

The consultation was concluded in April 2016. No revision to the advice was made. Why therefore do the supermarkets appear to have paid no heed?

This year I have been immensely impressed by Sauvignon Blanc wines from the Loire Valley in France. Not just the grand appellations of Pouilly-Fumé and Sancerre, but the generic wines marketed as Touraine. The New Zealand hegemony in this sector looks past. Mind you, it was surely the Kiwis' brilliance with Sauvignon that eventually woke French winemakers up in the first place.

The same probably goes for the wine industry in Spain. Rioja sails on serenely, but relatively obscure Spanish regions such as Priorat, Ribera del Duero and

Utiel-Requena are now putting serious-quality reds on supermarket shelves until recently crowded out by me-too brands from the New World. Aussie Chardonnay is giving way to scintillating dry whites from the Spanish regions of Rias Baixas and Rueda.

And white burgundy is proliferating too. All the supermarkets are seeking out these hugely improved wines, from a region once complacent that it made the most exclusive and expensive dry whites in the world, but has only just twigged to the opportunity to compete with its countless imitators in the mid-market – and win.

And then there's Italy. I see names like Aglianico, Bolgheri and Copertino on red-wine shelves once exclusively populated by Amarone, Barolo and Chianti. All these wines are potentially good, of course, but to genuine quality from Italy has been added genuine diversity. And Italy is potentially the most diverse wine-producing nation of them all.

And so on. Throughout the wine trade, these are pioneering times. The specialist merchants do lead the way, and it's been a marvel to see the independent companies, once facing annihilation by supermarket competition, regaining market share. I hope that anyone sufficiently interested in wine to be reading this book will also look beyond the supermarkets to the more adventurous precincts of the business. Merchants such as Berry Bros & Rudd – now run by ex-Tesco wine boss Dan Jago – come immediately to mind, along with Adnams of Southwold, Great Western Wine of Bath, Tanners of Shrewsbury and Townends of Hull. And no one serious about wine should fail to join that most diverse and democratic of operators, the Wine Society.

Back here among the aisles and online sites of the multiple giants meantime, I should explain the workings of this guide. First, the scoring system. I use a 0 to 10 scale, but it's not a strictly qualitative one, because I take into account the price of the wine. The official shelf price, that is. Supermarket wines are perpetually discounted, and this distorts my scoring system. In its defence, if you find a 9-scoring wine at £5.99 instead of the £7.99 I have noted, you will like it even better.

Please view my scores in the same spirit that I do. They are awarded on a subjective basis in full knowledge of the price. For the purposes of this book I do not taste 'blind' in the interests of any kind of objectivity. All but a very few of the wines listed carry scores of 8 or above. There just isn't space in a pocket-size book such as this (never visit the wine aisles without it) for angry denunciations of dire bottles. The very occasional sub-8 score goes to wines I have liked right enough, but have believed too expensive for what they are. Perhaps I am trying to will the retailer into a price reduction. Perhaps the wine will be included in a promotion. Be vigilant.

Wines scoring 8 are always good and good value. At 9, I am attributing special merit and particular value too. Maximum score goes to wines that I believe cannot be bettered in respect of character, quality and value – all three.

In my notes on the individual wines I am trying to explain their nature, usually by metaphorical means such as the evocations of fruit or other plant flavours, occasionally meandering into climatic and textural domains. Forgive me when I go too far. On a more mundane note, I include the alcohol-by-volume level for every wine that is below 12 or above 13 per cent.

A sense of place

This book categorises the wines by nation of origin. It is largely to follow the manner in which retailers arrange their wines, but also because it is the country or region of origin that still most distinguishes one style of wine from another. True, wines are now commonly labelled most prominently with their constituent grape variety, but to classify all the world's wines into the small number of principal grape varieties would make for categories of an unwieldy size.

Chardonnay, Sauvignon Blanc and Pinot Grigio are overwhelmingly dominant among whites, and four grapes – Cabernet Sauvignon, Grenache, Merlot and Syrah (also called Shiraz) – account for a high proportion of red wines made worldwide.

But each area of production still – in spite of creeping globalisation – puts its own mark on its wines. Chardonnays from France remain (for the moment at least) quite distinct from those of Australia. Cabernet Sauvignon grown in a cool climate such as that of Bordeaux is a very different wine from Cabernet cultivated in the cauldron of the Barossa.

Of course there are 'styles' that winemakers worldwide seek to follow. Yellow, oaky Chardonnays of the type pioneered in South Australia are now made in South Africa, too – and in new, high-tech wineries in New Zealand and Chile, Spain and Italy. But the variety is still wide. Even though the 'upfront' high-alcohol wines of the New World have grabbed so much of the market, France continues to make the elegant wines it has always made in its classic regions. Germany still produces racy, delicate Rieslings, and the distinctive zones of Italy, Portugal and Spain make ever more characterful wines from indigenous grapes, as opposed to imported global varieties.

Among less expensive wines, the theme is, admittedly, very much a varietal one. The main selling point for most 'everyday' wines is the grape of origin rather than the country of origin. It makes sense, because the characteristics of various grape varieties do a great deal to identify taste. A bottle of white wine labelled 'Chardonnay' can reasonably be counted on to deliver that distinctive peachy or pineappley smell and soft, unctuous apple flavours. A Sauvignon Blanc should evoke gooseberries, green fruit and grassy freshness. And so on.

For all the domination of Chardonnay and Cabernet, there are plenty of other grape varieties making their presence felt. Argentina, for example, has revived the fortunes of several French and Italian varieties that had become near-extinct at home. And the grape that (in my view) can make the most exciting of white wines, the Riesling, is now doing great things in the southern hemisphere as well as at home in Germany.

Among the current market trends, the rise of rosé continues apace. Now accounting for one out of every eight bottles of still wine sold, the choice of pink brands has simply exploded. I have certainly found a greater number of interesting pinks than might have been imagined a few years ago, but there are still plenty of dull ones with suspiciously high levels of residual sugar, so choose carefully.

Rosé wines are supposed to be made from black-skinned grapes. After the crush, the skins are left in contact with the juice for long enough to impart a pleasing colour, and maybe some flavour with it, and the liquids and solids are then separated before the winemaking process continues as it would for white wine.

Some rosés are made merely by blending red and white wines together. Oddly enough, this is how all (bar one or two) pink champagnes are made, as permitted under the local appellation rules. But under prevailing regulations in Europe, the practice is otherwise forbidden. Elsewhere in the world, where winemaking is very much less strictly standardised, blending is no doubt common enough.

It is, I know, a perpetual source of anguish to winemakers in tightly regulated European nations that they have to compete in important markets like Britain with producers in Australia, the Americas and South Africa who can make and label their wines just as they please. Vineyard irrigation, the use of oak chips, and the blending in of wines from other continents are all permitted in the New World and eschewed in the Old.

But would we have it any other way? No winemaker I have met in Bordeaux or Barolo, Bernkastel or Rias Baixas seriously wants to abandon the methods and conventions that make their products unique – even with an eye on creating a global brand. And in this present difficult economic climate for wine drinkers (and winemakers) worldwide, this assurance of enduring diversity is a comfort indeed.

Spot the grape variety

The character of most wines is defined largely by the grape variety, and it is a source of innocent pleasure to be able to identify which variety it is without peeking at the label. Here are some of the characteristics to look for in wines from the most widely planted varieties.

White

Chardonnay: Colour from pale to straw gold. Aroma can evoke peach, pineapple, sweet apple. Flavours of sweet apple, with creaminess or toffee from oak contact.

Fiano: Italian variety said to have been cultivated from ancient Roman times in the Campania region of southern Italy. Now widely planted on the mainland and in Sicily, it makes dry but soft wines of colours ranging from pale to pure gold with aromas of honey, orchard fruit, almonds and candied apricot. Well-made examples have beautifully balanced nutty-fresh flavours. Fiano is becoming fashionable.

Pinot Grigio: In its home territory of north-east Italy, it makes wines of pale colour, and pale flavour too. What makes the wine so popular might well be its natural low acidity. Better wines are more aromatic, even smoky, and pleasingly weighty in the manner of the Pinot Gris made in Alsace – now being convincingly imitated in both Argentina and New Zealand.

Riesling: In German wines, pale colour, sharp-apple aroma, racy fruit whether dry or sweet. Faint spritz common in young wines. Petrolly hint in older wines. Australian and New Zealand Rieslings have more colour and weight, and often a minerally, limey twang.

Sauvignon Blanc: In the dry wines, pale colour with suggestions of green. Aromas of asparagus, gooseberries, nettles, seagrass. Green, grassy fruit.

Semillon: Colour can be rich yellow. Aromas of tropical fruit including pineapple and banana. Even in dry wines, hints of honey amid fresh, fruit-salad flavours.

Viognier: Intense pale-gold colour. Aroma evokes apricots, blanched almonds and fruit blossom. Flavours include candied fruits. Finish often low in acidity.

Red

Cabernet Sauvignon: Dense colour, purple in youth. Strong aroma of blackcurrants and cedar wood ('cigar box'). Flavour concentrated, often edged with tannin so it grips the mouth.

Gamay: One of the most distinctive grapes of France, where it is the exclusive variety in the red wines of Beaujolais. Colour can be purple, with a suggestion of blue; nose evokes new-squashed raspberries, and there may be a hint of pear drops, an effect of carbonic maceration, a vinification technique used in Beaujolais. Fruit flavours are notably summery, juicy and refreshing.

Grenache: Best known in the Côtes du Rhône, it tends to make red wines pale in colour but forceful in flavour with a wild, hedgerow-fruit style and hints of pepper.

Malbec: Originally a Bordeaux variety, Malbec has become principally renowned in Argentina, where it thrives in the high-altitude vineyards of Mendoza. Wines are characterised by very dark, dense colour, and by aromas that perhaps fancifully evoke leather and liquorice as well as dark fruits. Flavours include black fruits with chocolate and spice; the wines are often grippy with retained tannin.

Merlot: Dark, rich colour. Aroma of sweet black cherry. Plummy, rich, mellow fruit can be akin to Cabernet but with less tannin. May be hints of bitter chocolate.

Pinot Noir: Colour distinctly pale, browning with age. Aromas of strawberry and raspberry. Light-bodied wine with soft-fruit flavours but dry, clean finish.

Sangiovese: The grape of Chianti and now of several other Italian regions, too. Colour is fine ruby, and may be relatively light; a plummy or even pruny smell is typical, and flavours can evoke blackcurrant, raspberry and nectarine. Tannin lingers, so the wine will have a dry, nutskin-like finish.

Shiraz or Syrah: Intense, near-black colour. Aroma of ripe fruit, sometimes spicy. Robust, rich flavours, commonly with high alcohol, but with soft tannins. The Shiraz of Australia is typically much more substantial than the Syrah of the south of France.

Tempranillo: Colour can be pale, as in Rioja. Blackcurrant aroma, often accompanied by vanilla from oak ageing. Tobacco, even leather, evoked in flavours.

There is more about all these varieties, and many others, in 'What wine words mean' starting on page 155.

Looking for a branded wine?

While the supermarkets' own-label wines – the likes of the Sainsbury's Taste the Difference and the Tesco Finest ranges – are obviously exclusive to the respective chains, branded wines are very often stocked by any number of different retailers.

If you're looking for a favourite brand, do check the index to this book on page 189. If I have tasted the wine and given it a mention, it is most likely to appear under the heading of the supermarket that hosted the tasting. But you might be accustomed to seeing this particular wine in another chain altogether.

I cannot give space in a pocket-sized book to repetitions of notes on popular brands that might very well be sold by each of the supermarket chains. But I do try to keep tasting the bestselling brands in hope of finding something positive to say about them.

My pick of
the year

Totting up the top scores after finalizing my choice of *The Best Wines in the Supermarkets* always provides a harmless frisson. Which retailer has come up with the maximum maxima? Which nation?

This year 26 wines have scored 10 out 10. The breakdown is as follows. There are 13 reds, 10 whites and 3 sparkling. The honours among the supermarkets are pretty even. Asda and Sainsbury's have 4 apiece; the Co-op, Marks & Spencer and Waitrose 3 each; Aldi, Majestic, Morrisons and Tesco are all on 2; and Lidl brings up the rear with 1.

Countries of origin are similarly distributed except for France, way ahead of the pack with 10; Australia, Chile, Italy and South Africa are joint runners-up with 3 apiece; Portugal has 2; Germany, New Zealand and Spain follow with 1 each.

Red wines

Estevez Cabernet Carmenère 2015	Aldi	£4.79
Beaujolais Alliance des Vignerons 2016	Morrisons	£5.00
Waitrose Good Ordinary Claret 2015	Waitrose	£5.19
Extra Special Carmenère 2016	Asda	£5.98
Extra Special Douro 2015	Asda	£5.98
Finest Faugères 2015	Tesco	£8.00
Lava Beneventano Aglianico 2012	Tesco	£8.50
Porta 6 Lisboa 2015	Majestic	£8.99
Priorat Noster Nobilis 2014	Asda	£9.28
Wirra Wirra Church Block Cabernet Sauvignon Shiraz Merlot 2014	Co-op	£10.49
Langhe Nebbiolo 2015	M&S	£11.00
Workshop McLaren Vale Shiraz 2015	Morrisons	£12.00
Château Lamothe Bergeron 2009	Co-op	£13.99

White wines

Bianco Vino da Tavola 2015	M&S	£5.00
Cimarosa South African Chenin Blanc 2016	Lidl	£3.89

Extra Special Chilean Sauvignon Blanc 2016	Asda	£5.98
Taste the Difference Côtes du Rhône White 2015	Sainsbury	£7.00
Taste the Difference Greco di Tufo 2016	Sainsbury	£9.00
Lot 18 Baden Pinot Blanc 2015	Aldi	£9.99
Craft 3 Adelaide Hills Chardonnay 2016	M&S	£10.00
Springfield Estate Special Cuvée Sauvignon Blanc 2016	Waitrose	£10.99
Seifried Grüner Veltliner 2016	M&S	£11.00
Stellenrust Stellenbosch Manor Chenin Blanc 2016	Sainsbury	£13.00
Domaine Schlumberger Alsace Grand Cru Pinot Gris 2013	Majestic	£17.99

Sparkling wines

Champagne Les Pionniers Brut	Co-op	£16.99
Winemakers' Selection Blanc de Noirs Champagne Brut	Sainsbury	£20.00
Waitrose Special Reserve Vintage Champagne 2005	Waitrose	£24.99

Aldi

Did you know? The name is a contraction of **Albrecht Diskont**, its gigantic German begetter, and it's pronounced AL dee, not ALL dee. It's the fastest-growing grocer in Britain: 750 stores now, 1,000 by 2022. It has lately overtaken Waitrose and the Co-op in overall sales, and now ranks number five, after the Big Four supermarkets.

The wines have only recently become of interest, but the proportion of worthwhile ones is growing fast, and price is by no means the sole attraction. Of the 40 wines I've picked out here all are exclusive to Aldi, and none costs above £10 a bottle.

This year's new wines include several from France's sun-baked Languedoc region made by celebrity *vigneron* Jean-Claude Mas, and some of them are worthy of the name. Likewise Aldi's expanding range of sparkling wines, from a proper champagne that's often under a tenner to no fewer than three proseccos I actually like. The two Aldi wines I've liked most, however, hail respectively from Chile and Germany. The excellent Estevez Cabernet Carmenère red at a risible £4.79 flies a defiant flag for the sub-fiver wine bargain, further endangered by 2017's duty/VAT hike past £2.50 per bottle for the first time. And the scintillating Pinot Blanc from Baden is an uplifting revelation of what this elusive grape variety, hardly known outside Alsace, can do. At £9.99, this wine is most certainly a bargain in its own way, and a legitimate indicator that Aldi is becoming a serious merchant. Just before going to press I found this prodigy reduced in one store to £6.99. What goes on?

I do like the attractively presented 'Lot Series' wines that form Aldi's premium range, and have included here a number of new additions. Also here are wines from the range that I tasted and liked last year and remain on sale. Several of these have been reduced from the set £9.99 price down to £6.99, and are well worth looking out for.

Last year I complained in this space that too many of the best Aldi wines were available online only from the chain's new home-delivery service. This time round, I'm glad to report, all the wines described here should be found in the stores as well as on the computer. This is real progress.

RED WINES

AUSTRALIA

8 **Exquisite Collection South Australian Shiraz 2016** £5.79
Old-fashioned extra-ripe up-front Aussie barbecue red at a fair price; 14% alcohol.

9 **Lot 10 Clare Coonawarra Cabernet Sauvignon 2014** £6.99
Price cut from £9.99 to £6.99 makes this harmonious, lushly dark and cassis-rich blend a brilliant bargain; 14% alcohol.

CHILE

10 Estevez Cabernet Carmenère 2015 £4.79
Hits the spot: bright, jewel-like ruby colour (the grape name Carmenère supposedly derives from the carmine hue imparted by its skins); ripe, wholesome blackcurrant perfume and corresponding gently-spiced flavours in ideal balance – brilliant value for a wine I cannot fault; 13.5% alcohol.

8 Estevez Pinot Noir 2016 £4.79
Pale but not wan and nicely defined ripe cherry style has plumpness and balance; healthy summer party red to consider drinking cool; 13.5% alcohol.

FRANCE

8 Vignobles Roussellet Pinot Noir £4.49
Standby non-vintage Vin de France has Beaujolais-like bounce and juiciness; try it gently chilled.

9 Jean Claude Mas Estate Malbec 2016 £6.99
My pick of the new Mas varietal wines is darkly juicy and wholesome with a gamey savour in the best Malbec tradition; not a heavyweight, but nicely integrated and ripe, with 13.5% alcohol.

9 **Lot 11 Metairie de Bois Corbières 2013**   £6.99
I'm repeating this from last year's edition on the off-chance any remains as Aldi have cut the price from £9.99 to £6.99. It's a silky Mediterranean smoothie, packed with lush black fruits, spice and toasty savour; 14.5% alcohol.

8 **Jean Claude Mas Origines Mount Baudile 2016**   £6.99
Bordeaux-type blend mostly Cabernet Sauvignon and Merlot from Languedoc makes for a vigorous, juicy spin on a claret theme with good weight and ripeness; 14% alcohol.

8 **Lot 22 Terrasses du Larzac 2015**   £9.99
Yet another J-C Mas production, this is a substantial, luxury-oaked Syrah–Grenache combo from a single vineyard near the seaside resort of Sète; dark mulberry-plummy baked fruit with warming spice and 14.5% alcohol.

8 **Lot 23 Minervois La Livinière 2015**   £9.99
Blood-coloured, pruny-nosed, darkly ripe and silkily spicy red-meat wine from Château Fauzan in prime Languedoc country has the garrigue savour of the region and comes in a handsome package; 14.5% alcohol.

8 **Falco Rosso Appassimento 2015**   £5.99
Dare I call this a novelty wine? It's made, Verona-style with the addition of a bit of concentrated grape must, in Puglia so you get darkness in colour and flavour and some nice dry grip to balance the slightly marzipanny richness; 14% alcohol.

FRANCE

ITALY

RED WINES

NEW ZEALAND

🍷 8 **Exquisite Collection New Zealand Pinot Noir 2014** £6.99

Mature Marlborough wine, very pale but bright with sweetly ripe perky red-cherry fruit; unserious but proper Kiwi Pinot at a keen price to enjoy cool; 13.5% alcohol.

SPAIN

🍷 8 **Toro Loco Superior 2015** £3.89

Perennial Tempranillo-based bargain from Utiel-Requena has abounding red-fruit flavours in wholesome balance.

🍷 8 **Gran Reserva Valdepeñas 2009** £4.99

Valdepeñas (Valley of the Stones) is an isolated vineyard zone amid the dusty vastness of Spain's great central plain La Mancha, producing Rioja-type, but rarely Rioja-quality, reds. Here's a mature but not decrepit oaky-blackcurranty example at a bargain price.

🍷 9 **Lot 06 Priorat 2014** £6.99

Left over from last year and cut from £9.99 to £6.99, a liquorice-rich pure Garnacha from the cult Priorat region brimming with dark intensity and savour; 14.5% alcohol.

PINK WINES

FRANCE

🍷 9 **Exquisite Collection Côtes de Provence Rosé 2016** £5.99

Pale shell-pink colour and alluring floral nose, dry but well short of austere, a convincing refresher that tastes truly pink, at a price for a Provence wine that for once offers true value too. Also in a party-size magnum at £12.99.

WHITE WINES

ARGENTINA

♟ 9 **Lot 21 Argentinian Chardonnay 2015** £9.99
The oak on this rich but mineral-bright Mendoza Chardonnay is evident but not overwhelming; an artful luxury wine in the burgundy style at a rather more approachable price, but with its own distinctive merits besides. For those who prefer white wine, a nifty match for Christmas turkey; 13.5% alcohol.

AUSTRALIA

♟ 9 **Exquisite Collection Clare Valley**
Riesling 2016 £6.99
Edgy and aromatic very-dry and limey Riesling in the authentic Aussie manner. This has been a consistent top buy at Aldi for several vintages in a row; 11% alcohol.

AUSTRIA

♟ 9 **Wachau Grüner Veltliner 2015** £6.99
Leaping trout on the label may be intended to suggest the mountain-stream freshness and minerality of this engaging dry and racy aperitif white; elegant and intriguing.

CHILE

♟ 8 **Estevez Chilean Chardonnay 2016** £4.99
Straight, ripe and wholesome unoaked varietal with a brassica note amid the customary peach and melon.

WHITE WINES

**8 Pardon My French Côtes de
Gascogne 2016** £4.99
Respectable dry and freshly crisp party wine unenhanced
by superannuated jokey nomenclature; 11.5% alcohol.

**9 Exquisite Collection Touraine
Sauvignon Blanc 2016** £5.49
These generic Loire Valley varietals often easily match
their New Zealand rivals for interest and far outdo them
for value; this is water-white but shiningly brisk and
tangy with grassy-briny fruit and palpable purity.

**8 Jean Claude Mas Classic Organic Vin
Blanc 2016** £5.99
Sunny melon-sweet nose to this rather lush Pays d'Oc dry
and virtuous wine gives way to balanced tropical-sweet-
apple fruit and finishes crisp; good food white, it will go
with anything.

**8 Exquisite Collection Limoux
Chardonnay 2015** £6.99
Worthy successor to last year's sherbetty/sweet-apple 2014
vintage; dry but mellow from a Languedoc appellation
that devotes most of its Chardonnay to sparkling wine;
13.5% alcohol.

8 The Forgotten One Haut Poitou 2016 £6.99
Pure Loire Valley Sauvignon Blanc has seagrassy freshness
and generous, ripe, typical fruit; I forget the origin of the
cryptic name.

WHITE WINES

GERMANY

🍷 **10** **Lot 18 Baden Pinot Blanc 2015**   £9.99
Well-coloured food white (poultry, creamy pasta and rice, fish, you name it) from Germany's sunniest wine region with a heavenly herby-lemony-canteloupe nose and plump, softly spicy orchard fruit; dry, exotic, and a rare treat. I'm giving it max points partly to applaud this triumphant application of the elusive Pinot Blanc grape. Given Aldi's origins, why don't they offer more German wines? Late news: I have found this in store reduced to £6.99.

🍷 **8** **Grillo Sauvignon Blanc**   £4.99
Non-vintage Sicilian Sauvignon, dry and delicate but with a discreet almondy richness; nice creamy pasta matcher and friend to shellfish.

ITALY

🍷 **9** **Exquisite Collection Gavi 2016**   £5.49
Nice bit of brassica amid the tropical-fruit ripeness and nutty creaminess in this paradoxically dry Piedmontese food white; you get a lot of interest for not a lot of money.

🍷 **8** **Grande Alberone Chardonnay 2016**   £5.49
This sunnily ripe and friendly dry Sicilian blend is actually just four parts Chardonnay, the other six being island natives Catarratto and Inzolia.

N. ZEALAND

🍷 **8** **Freeman's Bay Sauvignon Blanc 2016**   £5.59
Down in price from last year's £5.89 this Marlborough perennial nevertheless impressed me less than the 10-scoring 2015. Decent pea-green Sauvignon soup in a safe, tangy style.

WHITE WINES

8 Animus Vinho Verde 2016 £4.99
Likeable apple-citrus brightness in this just-prickly, just off-dry delicate refresher from the Minho Valley's 'green wine' zone; touristy twist on the true bone-dry vinho verde style, better than most; 10.5% alcohol.

8 Toro Loco Blanco 2016 £3.99
Eager green-fruited but craftily lush party dry white from the Viura grape of oaky white Rioja fame, here made in less-vaunted Valencian Utiel-Requena region; 11.5% alcohol.

9 Exquisite Collection Rias Baixas Albariño 2016 £5.99
Tangy seaside dry wine in the authentic style of Atlantic Spain's blustery Rias Baixas region; fine racy example at a keen price.

8 The Wine Foundry Godello 2016 £6.49
Godello is the go-to grape in Spain's northwest, making dry whites compared by the cognoscenti to those of Burgundy. Try this jazzily labelled example, claiming to evoke 'crisp lemons and honeysuckle blossom' and doing exactly that.

SPARKLING WINES

🍷 **9 Philippe Michel Crémant du Jura 2014**　　£7.49
Another cracking vintage for this Aldi perennial, still a terrific bargain (up just 20p on last year and £2 on the memorable 2004 vintage in 2008) full of crispy-creamy Chardonnay vivacity carried along in the stream of consistent foam to a fine, fresh finish. Smart package, now in the Exquisite Collection range.

🍷 **9 Crémant de Loire Blanc de Noir**　　£7.99
New brut-dry white sparkler made entirely from black Cabernet Franc grapes – better known for Loire still reds Chinon and Saumur – to great effect, alive with redcurrant juiciness and orchardy freshness, and rushing with eager bubbles in the authentic crémant ('creaming') manner.

🍷 **9 Veuve Monsigny Champagne Brut**　　£10.00
A fine gold colour and wholesome yeasty nose invite you into Aldi's house champagne, following up with generous fruit balanced with briskness; always fun and usually a bargain at its ever-changing price.

🍷 **8 Valdobbiadene Prosecco Superiore**　　£7.49
Universal brand of the trendy tank-made Venetian fizz has elderflower perfume, plenty of lively foam, crisp-pear fruit and a brisk, dry style; 11.5% alcohol.

🍷 **8 Organic Prosecco 2016**　　£7.99
This vintage prosecco from organically cultivated grapes is a novelty, as is the evident quality of this lively and cleanly dry elderflower-scented fun fizz in an antique-style bottle. I must confess I did like it; 11.5% alcohol.

SPARKLING WINES

ITALY

🍷 8 **Belletti Prosecco 1.5 litre** £12.99

Party-piece magnum size at a fair price; pale, persistently frothy and soft in its peary fruitiness. It is not 'extra dry' as claimed, but it's not entirely lacking in acidity either; 11% alcohol.

Asda

First things first. Asda has more true wine bargains than any other supermarket. There are masses of great buys under £6 and even under £5, and if you're shopping to a price, this is the first place to look. Neither Aldi nor Lidl comes close. And in common with all its rivals, barring Aldi and Lidl of course, Asda does frequent price promotions – more usually on individual wines than across the range.

Most of the wines reviewed here are from Asda's flagship own-label range under the Extra Special branding. Well they're not *all* extra special but they are impressively consistent and by no means expensive, starting at not much above a fiver. Italian reds are currently very good, including two terrific Primitivos, a very cheap Chianti Classico Riserva and even a real Lambrusco.

In tandem with the growing Extra Special range is the more recently added (2015) Wine Atlas collection of own-label wines. They feature themed labels drawing on the poster style of the 1920s travel industry, and they look a treat. I've particularly picked out two red wines, Wine Atlas Ventoux from the Rhône Valley, and a Negroamaro from Puglia in Italy's 'heel' – both under £6 and tasting well above that.

When you're as big as Asda – the Leeds-based chain has been US giant Walmart's UK offshoot since 1999 and is part of the world's largest retail organization – you can be forgiven, I suppose, for not adopting a universal stocking policy. In the wine aisles, there is a considerable variation in the variety of wines on offer. My own nearest store is hopeless. Stick to the bigger stores, or look online.

I can heartily recommend the Asda 'Wine Shop' website from which I have successfully ordered for home delivery on more than one occasion. It's easy to use, includes most of the wines (I think) and offers discounts on many of them. You can buy by the individual bottle and for sensibly sized orders (currently £40 and above) delivery is free – and fast.

RED WINES

Asda

ARGENTINA

🍷 8 **Extra Special Malbec 2016** £5.98
The trademark leather-upholstery whiff comes clearly from this plummy-roasty Mendoza Malbec with reassuring familiarity; juicy ripeness and a good grip of tannin.

AUSTRALIA

🍷 8 **Busby Premium Shiraz 2016** £4.88
Apparently oaked Limestone Coast wine packs a lot of complex ripe berry-fruit flavours for this very modest price; wholesome and nicely finished, with 14.5% alcohol.

🍷 8 **Zilzie Shiraz Viognier 2016** £5.18
A famous Australian winemaker told me with a straight face that he added small measures of white Viognier must to his deep red Shiraz must to make his wine 'more feminine'. This powerful purple brambly and velvety bargain red illustrates the point; 14% alcohol.

🍷 8 **Extra Special Pinot Noir 2016** £7.98
Bright in its cherry colour and healthy strawberry freshness, a poised middleweight Yarra Valley Pinot by De Bortoli; I wouldn't be afraid to serve this chilled.

🍷 8 **Barossa Ink Shiraz 2015** £9.98
Made by redoubtable Grant Burge, this indeed has an inky look to it, and corresponding woof in the opulent black fruit, but it has lifting fruit nuance and a brisk balancing acidity; 14% alcohol.

RED WINES

8 Extra Special Chilean Pinot Noir 2016 £5.28
Pale and delicate Aconcagua wine with a bright cherry perfume and matching firm fruit; brisk, balanced and refreshing when served chilled; 14% alcohol.

10 Extra Special Carmenère 2016 £5.98
Attractive intense colour could be described as carmine (origin of the grape's name) and the attractive intense flavours are decidely delicious; luscious chocolate-centred hedgerow fruits busy with spice and savour, a grown-up and underpriced Colchagua wine to match steaks and grills; 13.5% alcohol.

9 Errazuriz Merlot 2016 £8.98
Curico producer Errazuriz is renowned for its Merlot and this one makes the case. Rich and sleek with vivid fruits, it's beautifully made and bears comparison with Bordeaux wines such as Pomerol costing many times this price.

8 Wine Atlas Minervois 2015 £5.48
This Syrah-led blackberry Languedoc wine has a warming spice and liquorice heart to the ripe flavour; 13.5% alcohol. Good match for hearty stews, sausages and starchy bean cuisine.

9 Wine Atlas Ventoux 2015 £5.98
Instantly likeable well-knit Rhône red; has spicy intensity and long flavours with what feels like a vanilla richness from oak contact; 14% alcohol. Good value.

8 Extra Special Saint-Emilion 2015 £8.98
This young, but already forward, intensely-coloured claret is silkily ripe and elegant. St-Emilion wines do evolve faster than those of other Bordeaux zones and this is genuinely good drinking now; a class act.

CHILE

FRANCE

RED WINES

9 **Wine Atlas Negroamaro 2016** £4.98

Sun-baked black fruits take on an extra toasty savour and almond richness in this big juicy Puglian varietal with a ripe 14% alcohol. Classy winter-warming wine at a very good price.

9 **Orbitali Squinzano Riserva 2012** £5.00

Squinzano is a remote little burg and DOC in Puglia. Asda has listed this one for several years and consistently lowered the price. I paid just £4 for mine. Which makes this darkly smooth and savoury, gently baked, spicy and comforting Negroamaro red a brilliant bargain. If you can find any.

9 **Orbitali Primitivo 2015** £5.28

Cockle-warming Puglian with smooth summer red-fruit ripeness in a well-knit texture of firm dark savour; tastes oak-matured, which surprises me at this price. Ace pizza red.

8 **Extra Special Barbera d'Asti 2014** £5.48

This brisk purple Piedmont red has blueberry bounce and an acidity close to austere, which makes it a magic match for sticky pasta dishes.

9 **Extra Special Primitivo 2015** £5.78

Blood-red Puglian has seriously intense, cushiony-plump truffle-cassis-blueberry fruit with (it says in my note) weight and conviction; 13.5% alcohol. Great value and a useful match for spicy or starchy menus.

RED WINES

**9 Extra Special Chianti Classico
Riserva 2012**   £5.98
Good-value mature wine has a sweetly beckoning
strawberry whiff in the Chianti manner, well integrated
black berry and cherry fruit with a vanilla creaminess and
proper nutskin-dry finish; 13.5% alcohol.

9 Solato Lambrusco   £6.98
Real Lambrusco! This is a dry, very slightly spritzy,
red intended for drinking chilled and it's a good one:
bouncing red-berry fruit with violet perfume finishing
very dry, almost astringent; fantastic picnic wine; 11%
alcohol.

8 Extra Special Morellino di Scansano 2016   £7.48
Scansano is a village DOCG in maritime Tuscany where
the Sangiovese grape (of local Chianti fame) makes this
distinctively rounded wine weighty with morello (as in
the name perhaps) black cherry fruit and taut acidity;
13.5% alcohol.

8 Extra Special Valpolicella Ripasso 2014   £8.98
Good example of the dried-grape-boosted Verona wine
has the right gently abrasive black-cherry fruit with spicy
core and very dry finish; 14% alcohol.

8 Sensi Orbitali Bolgheri 2015   £10.48
Super-Tuscan red from 4 parts Cabernet/Merlot to 1 of
local Sangiovese; defined dark savours to the deep cassis
fruits; 14% alcohol.

ITALY

RED WINES

Asda

PORTUGAL

🍷 10 Extra Special Douro 2015 £5.98
The Douro Valley – Port country – has become a deeply likeable source of ripe and warming table reds. This is my favourite of the year: integrated dark oak-smoothed savours of the Douro's own spicy variation on the 'garrigue' of Provence with weight, mint and silkiness, and all for under six quid; 13.5% alcohol.

S.AFRICA

🍷 8 Extra Special Fairtrade Pinotage 2016 £5.78
Good to see Asda taking up the Fairtrade cause and this is a very fair wine, deep-coloured classic Pinotage with plummy-roasty depths and signature tarry tinge; 14.5% alcohol.

SPAIN

🍷 8 Wine Atlas Bobal 2015 £4.98
All-purpose fragrant cherry-strawberry somehow typically Spanish red wine from the obscure Bobal grape cultivated in similarly obscure Utiel-Requena region (a wild landscape west of Valencia well worth a visit); plump and wholesome.

🍷 9 Extra Special Garnacha 2015 £5.00
Juicy and satisfying Carinena varietal scores for charm as much as for cheapness; 14% alcohol.

**🍷 8 Extra Special Marques del Norte
Rioja Reserva 2013** £6.28
Notably inexpensive for a mature Reserva Rioja this still seems in a lively youth, with the vivid blackcurrant fruit well on top of the oak; 14% alcohol. See if you can detect Asda's own note of 'balsamic, toast and leather' in the aroma.

RED WINES

SPAIN

🍷 **9** **Casa Luis Gran Reserva 2011** £6.48
The still-bright fruit in this mature Carinena wine clearly evokes a rich blackcurrant crumble with plenty of cream poured over the top; lovely stuff at a very good price; 13.5% alcohol.

🍷 **10** **Priorat Noster Nobilis 2014** £9.28
Perennial favourite in a terrific new vintage is already rounding out, showing truffly, gamey, ripe nuances in the lush blackberry and plum fruits; 15% alcohol. Price is up a bit on last year's £7.98 for the 2013 but remains an absolute bargain for well-made wine from this very sought-after region.

PINK WINES

AUSTRALIA

🍷 **8** **Extra Special Sangiovese Rosé 2016** £8.98
Pale salmon colour to this surprise pink from King Valley in Australia's Victoria State, where Italian grape varieties proliferate. From the grape of Chianti this is red-berry-fruit wine with firm pink flavours and a brisk acidity; nice partner for a prawn from the barbie.

FRANCE

🍷 **8** **Sancerre Rosé 2016** £11.48
An indulgent rosé from a grand Loire appellation, this is a poised Pinot Noir, pale salmon and lively with crisp raspberry-strawberry fruit and a clear citrus edge; smart and refreshing.

SPAIN

🍷 **8** **Espartero Rioja Rosé 2016** £4.78
Boldly coloured and soft-summer-fruit flavoured dry style for positive refreshment at a sensible price; 14% alcohol.

WHITE WINES

Asda

AUSTRALIA

8 **Extra Special Chardonnay 2016** £5.78
Agreeable aromas of cabbage and melon ease you into a friendly, uncomplicated Barossa wine plump with peachy-creamy fruit and a mineral freshness; 13.5% alcohol.

CHILE

10 **Extra Special Chilean Sauvignon Blanc 2016** £5.98
Leyda wine comes in a very heavy retro-style bottle and delivers a corresponding abundance of lush asparagussy aromas and flavours; prolifically delicious and nuanced Sauvignon in the best ripe Chilean tradition and yet in sublime balance. I think I have tasted this same wine under the banner of at least one other supermarket, but Asda's price beats them all. Top marks.

8 **Winemaker's Choice Côtes de Gascogne 2016** £4.78
Smelled to me of Sauvignon and turned out to be Gascon regulars Gros Manseng and Colombard; it does have grassy tang and citrus freshness and sunny orchard-fruit ripeness too; 11.5% alcohol.

FRANCE

8 **Extra Special Bourgogne Chardonnay 2015** £9.48
Well-coloured blossom-nosed sweet-apple and peach pure Chardonnay has expensive oaky richness abutting the mineral purity; tastes like white burgundy.

WHITE WINES

FRANCE

🍷 9　**Extra Special Pouilly Fumé 2016**　　£10.98
Sauvignon Blanc might have become ubiquitous across
the world, but in the vineyards of Pouilly-sur-Loire it still
makes wines of a unique nature. Try this for its dappled
sunlight on the crystal river freshness (oh yes, it inspires
the pastoral notion) and complex green fruit aromas in
profusion; too delicious to delineate.

🍷 8　**Extra Special Chablis 2015**　　£11.48
Proper gold-shot-with-green colour to this lively flinty
pure Chardonnay from the famed northern outpost
of Burgundy, with a saucy leesy richness to the fruit;
warrants the price.

ITALY

🍷 8　**Extra Special Pinot Grigio 2016**　　£5.48
If you're still into PG try this one from sub-Alpine
Trentino for its encouragingly gold colour and perky
orchard fruit and even a trace of the smoky spiciness that
is supposed to be the grape's signature.

🍷 8　**Extra Special Gavi 2016**　　£6.78
Good of its kind – which means it's a crisp-pear-fresh,
lively and lasting dry white from Piedmont that's a good
friend to fish and creamy pasta dishes.

🍷 8　**Lugana 2016**　　£8.98
Lush Lake Garda dry white with yellow colour, ripe
peach fruit and an exotic tropical note; elegant flavours
that draw you in.

WHITE WINES

N. ZEALAND

🍷 **8** **Extra Special Sauvignon Blanc 2016** £6.48
Signature peapod scent (I like peapod myself) on this conservative Marlborough wine, gently tangy with gooseberries and nettles but not too green.

SPAIN

🍷 **8** **Extra Special Rueda 2016** £5.28
Pure Verdejo grape as is now the norm in Rueda, this also has the region's irresistible brightness of flavour, scintillating freshness and citrus twang.

SPARKLING WINES

FRANCE

🍷 **8** **Extra Special Champagne Brut** £16.00
Yeasty aroma, mellow fruit, eager tiny-bubble mousse make for a fine mature-tasting champagne with a big measure of Pinot Meunier grape and a modest price.

🍷 **9** **Extra Special Vintage Champagne Brut 2007** £22.00
Generous in colour and with bready aromas, a nicely evolved wine, softly ripe and comforting but with busy mousse, lively and inspiring. Good price for a decade-old champagne of this quality.

ITALY

🍷 **7** **Extra Special Prosecco** £8.98
Unexpected green perfume and a welcome freshness to this near-dry peary Veneto confection; 11.5% alcohol.

SPAIN

🍷 **9** **Extra Special Cava Rosado Brut 2014** £7.98
Floating amid the ocean of sticky white prosecco here's a really good pink product from Catalonia. Smoked-salmon colour, a bang of bright, strawberry-fresh full fizz all in crisp, clean, wholesome style.

—The Co-operative—

Several of my top buys at the Co-op this year are from the 'Irresistible' own-label range. This brand was introduced for wines about five years ago under the original heading of 'Truly Irresistible', and seems to be steadily improving in variety and interest. This contraction of the name is an improvement in itself.

Buying own-brand products at the Co-op has been given a further allure under the revamped Membership scheme. As Simon Cairns, category manager for wines, beers and spirits explains it, when members buy 'any own brand product or service from Co-op, 5% of what they spend will go back into an online wallet which can be spent at any time off future purchases'. That's a very much better deal than your bog-standard loyalty card.

And there's plenty to choose from. Irresistible Barbera d'Asti 2014 from Italy at £6.99 is a plum, Irresistible Leyda Valley Sauvignon Blanc 2016 from Chile at £7.49 is a peach, and Les Pionniers Champagne Brut at £16.99, named in honour of the Pioneers who founded the Co-operative Movement back in the day, is my supermarket bargain champagne of the year.

Shopping for wine at the Co-op needs to be done in person, as there is no dedicated online service for home delivery. There's a drawback here, because the 4,000-plus Co-op retail outlets across the country vary radically in the number of different wines they offer.

Some of the wines I have recommended here are listed available in 'fewer than 100' stores. These I have delineated with the note: megastores only. By which I mean Co-op superstores. Other wines are described as available in 'fewer than 1,000 stores'. This really means outlets on a supermarket scale as distinct from a convenience-shop scale.

Happy hunting.

RED WINES

ARGENTINA

🍷 9   **Co-op Fairtrade Cabernet Sauvignon 2015   £5.99**
A vigorous and generously ripe upfront-fruity blackcurranty food red which feels confidently made, with the added merit of production by leading Fairtrade estate La Riojana in the Famatina Valley. An admirable wine in every way.

🍷 8   **Co-op Irresistible Fairtrade Malbec 2015   £6.99**
Dark, dense-oaked pure Malbec by La Riojana with the trademark leather-scented roasty black-fruit flavours; good match for spicy-meaty-beany dishes.

🍷 8   **Don David Blend of Terroirs Malbec 2015   £8.99**
Smart-looking package named in honour of pioneering winemaker David Michel. Deep, deep purple colour and sinewy, ripe, sun-baked plummy fruit flavours; it's unoaked and convincingly pure in its varietal appeal; 14% alcohol.

AUSTRALIA

🍷 9   **The Unexpected Red 2016   £6.49**
I never know what to expect of gimmicky wines, but it's usually disappointment. Not this time. By Andrew Peace, it's mainly Cabernet Sauvignon with Sagrantino, the arch-tannic Italian variety, making a healthily ripe and yielding but firm black-fruit food red with oaky creaminess, a nice Italian-style dry finish and satisfying weight; 14% alcohol.

🍷 8   **The Black Shiraz 2016   £7.99**
Well, it's a deep purple rather than black, but comes with a nice toasty turn to the bumper blackberry fruit, big in flavour (and 14.5% alcohol) to make a nice match with saucy stews.

RED WINES

The Co-operative

AUSTRALIA

🏆 **10** **Wirra Wirra Church Block Cabernet Sauvignon Shiraz Merlot 2014** £10.49

Top McLaren Vale blend in fantastic form is thrillingly perfumed, full of vivid black fruits, ideally weighted and balanced. It's alive with joyful flavours and yet naturally elegant. World-class wine at a very fair price and 14.5% alcohol. Megastores only.

🏆 **9** **Henry's Drive Padthaway Shiraz 2012** £16.99

Super-sleek silky and spicy Limestone Coast classic owing much to the style of northern Rhône Syrahs such as Côte Rôtie. Still firmly tannic, this is already drinking beautifully but should develop for donkey's years; 14.5% alcohol.

CHILE

🏆 **8** **Co-op Irresistible Casablanca Pinot Noir 2016** £7.99

Warmly earthy Pinot in the proper Chilean manner with strawberry-sweet ripeness and fine, lifting acidity; 13.5% alcohol.

FRANCE

🏆 **9** **Les Hauts de Saint Martin Saint-Chinian 2015** £6.99

From the enterprising co-operative of Roquebrun in the craggiest heights of the Languedoc, this has all the dark, spicy, fruits-of-the-forest style hoped for, and a wholesome weightiness; nice match for barbecue offerings and starchy stews. Megastores only.

🏆 **8** **Château Vieux Manoir 2015** £6.99

Eye-catching Bordeaux delivering youthfully vigorous and eagerly perfumed black-fruit flavours with appreciable weight and intensity; jolly decent claret at a sensible price; 14% alcohol.

RED WINES

FRANCE

🍷 **8** **Château D'Auzanet 2016** **£7.99**
Dense maroon colour and crunchy but developed black
fruits in this 'Vin Bio' – organically grown – generic
Bordeaux make for a lively and balanced claret to match
red meat or game; 13.5% alcohol.

🍷 **8** **Château Jouanin 2012** **£8.99**
From the Bordeaux outpost of Castillon, this has the
sweet raisiny whiff of a maturing wine and lots of plump
cherry-blackberry fruit; juicy and approachable and
13.5% alcohol.

🍷 **10** **Château Lamothe-Bergeron 2009** **£13.99**
My pick from the Co-op's claret line-up, but the priciest,
natch. From fabled 2009 vintage and browning just a tad
at the colour rim, it's a well-known Haut-Médoc estate
with 'Cru Bourgeois' status showing an alluring cedary-
cassis nose ahead of complex, supple flavours of real
charm; the price seems more than reasonable for classy
claret; 13.5% alcohol. Megastores only.

🍷 **8** **Crozes-Hermitage Les Launes 2015** **£13.99**
Made by Delas, this inky-purple, all-Syrah, semi-precious
Rhône delivers the tell-tale raspberry-syrup Crozes nose,
leading into a welcome intense, full-fruit style (Crozes can
be stringy) with a dark savoury centre and grippy finish;
OK now, better in a couple of years; 13.5% alcohol.
Megastores only.

RED WINES

The Co-operative

FRANCE

🍷 **8** **Domaine Les Grandes Costes Pic
Saint Loup 2013** £14.99
Pic St Loup, soon to be elevated to AOC status, is now
the Languedoc's most garlanded name; leading to, I
believe, the high price of this Syrah-dominated wine. It's
a cracker, though, richly ripe blackberry silked up with
oak contact and already well developed; 14.5% alcohol.
Megastores only.

🍷 **9** **Torrebruna Primitivo 2015** £5.99
Sicilian spin on early-ripening Primitivo has sweet dark
savour in depth and a poised balance, nicely finished with
a proper Italian nutskin dryness. Smart heraldic label and
a very keen price.

ITALY

🍷 **8** **Co-op Irresistible Barbera d'Asti 2014** £6.99
Ripe intensity and firmness of brambly fruit in this juicy
Piedmont wine by dependable Araldica; 14% alcohol. I
much preferred it to the shorter if less expensive Co-op
Barbera, also by Araldica.

🍷 **8** **Villa Boscorotondo Chianti Classico
Riserva 2014** £15.99
Fine poised pungently black-fruity oak-aged Chianti by
lofty producer Castello Vicchiomaggio is rich, nuanced
and sleek; 13.5% alcohol. For a special occasion, a safe
investment. Megastores only.

RED WINES

SOUTH AFRICA

♈ 9 **KWV Cinsaut 2016** £7.99

Pale colour like Pinot Noir, but this is pure Cinsaut, a Mediterranean grape long cultivated in the Cape as a blending variety, and the parent (along with Pinot Noir) of South Africa's very own Pinotage vine. As the wordy label loudly declares, this wine evokes vanilla pod (it's oaked), dark cherry and ripe strawberry. It's also perky, wholesome, lipsmacking and distinctive with 13.5% alcohol. Give it a try.

SPAIN

♈ 8 **Marqués de Valido Rioja Reserva 2012** £8.99

New brand (to me) by ubiquitous Rioja giant Muriel, this is light in weight but generous with its sweetly oaked cassis fruit.

WHITE WINES

ARGENTINA

♈ 8 **Olas Torrontes Pinot Grigio 2016** £6.49

Fun dry party white has some elusive grapy succulence from Torrontes (Argentina's own white grape variety) and white-peach freshness besides.

AUSTRALIA

♈ 9 **Co-op Irresistible Australian Chardonnay 2016** £6.99

Old-fashioned label design predicts the style of this creamily oaked outdoor wine, which happily turns out much fresher and livelier than the over-ripe Aussie Chardys of the bad old days. Very pleasant surprise.

WHITE WINES

8 Parallel Vines 2016   **£6.99**
Plumply ripe dry blend by prolific Aussie winemaker
Andrew Peace is 7 parts Victoria State Chardonnay and
3 Marlborough (yes, New Zealand) Sauvignon Blanc. A
crafty concoction that curious wine lovers should try.

8 Berton Vineyards The Vermentino 2016   **£7.49**
Quite a restrained variation on the Corsican way with
Vermentino grapes, this has zest and plenty of crisp
orchard fruit.

8 Jim Barry The Lodge Hill Riesling 2016   **£9.99**
Famous Clare Valley wine; brisk and racy with a rush of
white-apple fruit and a bracing background of lime; classic
food white – especially Asian dishes – on good form.

**9 Co-op Irresistible Leyda Valley Sauvignon
Blanc 2016**   **£7.49**
Asparagus at the front of the complex aroma is followed
by generous corresponding flavours carried along with
near-spritzy grassy Sauvignon zest; ripe but lemon-twang
fresh at the finish; 13.5% alcohol.

8 Montes Chardonnay Reserva 2015   **£7.99**
Likeable brassica and stone-fruit perfume lifts this
lavishly oaked Curico Valley varietal full of sunny sweet-
apple fruits; 13.5% alcohol.

9 Domaine Lasserre Jurançon 2014 375ml   **£6.99**
Let's hear it for sweet wine! This half bottle from the
foothills of the Pyrenees has gold colour, an ambrosial
aroma and pure-gold honeyed fruit with a lifting citrus
acidity. It's positively fresh and a candidate for aperitif
duties as well as pud, blue cheese or foie-gras pairing.

AUSTRALIA

CHILE

FRANCE

The Co-operative

WHITE WINES

9 La Vieille Ferme Blanc 2016   **£6.99**
Popular brand from the famed Perrin family of the southern Rhône includes a measure of new-oak-raised wine imparting peachy plushness to the vivid, fresh and crisp style; 13.5% alcohol, consistently delicious, and given added allure by the label, adorned with chickens. Waitrose also have this wine, at £7.99.

8 Mâcon-Villages Chardonnay Cave de Lugny 2015   **£7.99**
This particularly sunny-ripe, minerally, southern burgundy from the excellent co-operative at Lugny is long, luscious and trimmed with a refreshing limey acidity; 13.5% alcohol.

8 Kleine Kapelle Pinot Grigio 2016   **£5.99**
Artful contrivance from the Rhine vineyards which not only mimics but even improves on the Italian original; a bit of almondy richness, even a smoky suggestion, to the orchard fruit, dry and brisk.

8 Reichsgraf von Kesselstatt Goldtröpfchen Kabinett Riesling 2014   **£10.99**
Traditional Moselle with fine colour, sweet mint, apple and lime aromas and racy Riesling fruit with a proper grapy lushness all in elegant balance; 8.5% alcohol.

8 Verdicchio dei Castelli di Jesi Piersanti 2016   **£5.79**
Botticelli's Venus is emblematic on this brisk, fleetingly herbaceous dry white from the Marche; good price and a nice match for scallops maybe.

WHITE WINES

9 Vanita Grillo 2016 £6.99

Stand-out grown-up Grillo – Sicily's signature dry white grape of the moment – with briskness and a twang of Sauvignon-like grassiness; exotic back flavours hint at grapefruit and white peach.

8 Co-op Irresistible Broglia Gavi 2016 £7.99

Minerally Piedmont dry wine has notions of honey and blanched nut and a well-judged citrus edge; 13.5% alcohol.

8 Co-op Irresistible Explorers Sauvignon Blanc 2016 £7.49

Dependable Marlborough perennial, flush with grassy-gooseberry flavours and delivering a well-defined freshness.

9 Peter Yealands Sauvignon Blanc 2016 £8.99

Marlborough estate Yealands continues to merit its garlands: this offers a fascinating mélange of green aromas and flavours including, I promise, artichoke, and the overall scintillating effect is greater than the sum of its parts.

7 Escudo Real Vinho Verde 2016 £5.99

Near-water-white, fractionally spritzy, marshmallowy dry white is fresh rather than 'green' and just 9.5% alcohol.

8 KWV Grenache Blanc 2016 £7.99

Noisy typographical label might lower expectations but this is a thoroughly likeable sunny dry white, lush with peachy fruit, long in flavour and neatly balanced by citrus acidity; 14% alcohol.

ITALY

NEW ZEALAND

PORTUGAL

S. AFRICA

The Co-operative

WHITE WINES

SOUTH AFRICA

8 **Stonehaven Sauvignon Blanc 2017** £7.99
Bright gooseberry nose and an eager rush of grassy-nettly
fruit in the textbook Cape Sauvignon – not too green and
in poised balance.

9 **Bosman Adama 2016** £9.99
Chenin Blanc is to the fore in this extravagantly-oaked
multi-variety blend showing toasty-honeyed-tropical
flavours artfully balanced with zesty citrus; it's a Fairtrade
wine, 13.5% alcohol, and a delight.

SPAIN

8 **Most Wanted Albariño 2016** £8.49
Newish brand from Rias Baixas has an authentic Atlantic
seagrass perfume and tang incorporating generous ripe
green fruits in the authentic regional manner.

SPARKLING WINES

FRANCE

10 **Champagne Les Pionniers Brut** £16.99
Made by Piper Heidsieck for the Co-op and
commemorating the 19th-century Pioneers of the Co-
operative Movement, this has a fine gold colour, big
promising bakery nose and the full gamut of mellow
champagne fruit flavours. Always a top buy it seems on
exceptional form right now, and the price is unbeatable.

8 **Champagne Les Pionniers 2008 Brut** £25.99
Vintage version of the great NV above, this has a buttery
scrambled-egg-on-toast aroma and long, rich flavours.
Charming mature fizz fairly priced.

SPARKLING WINES

7 Borgo Molino Venti 2 Prosecco £9.99
ITALY
Posh black bottle comes in matching gift box and delivers a soft (rather than sweet) pear-elderflower foam of friendly fruitiness; 11% alcohol.

8 Co-op Irresistible Cava Brut £6.99
SPAIN
Distinctly crisp, near-austere dry full sparkler with freshness and zest looks good value; 11.5% alcohol.

Lidl

The wine range at Lidl is divided neatly into two halves. There is the 'core' range of wines available all year round. And there is the Wine Cellar, a changing selection offered as parcels on the basis that when they're gone, they're gone. Six times a year (I reckon) a whole new Wine Cellar range is brought in. The whole lot always seems to sell out pretty fast.

For a guide such as this, published just once a year, the Wine Cellar concept presents a problem. Even wines I have tasted just a few weeks in advance of publication will have sold out before we get into print.

All the wines mentioned in the following pages are therefore from the 'core' range. They are by no means the most exciting you will find at your local Lidl, but I am assured that improvements are under way to the permanent range, and I believe I am already seeing signs of them.

Watch this space.

RED WINES

CHILE

🍷 9 Cimarosa Chile Malbec Reserva
Privada 2014 £4.49

This agreeable full-of-fruit middleweight has signature Malbec darkness and rather undersells itself with standard Lidl Cimarosa branding and needlessly paltry price. Look out for the 'Reserva Privada' designation small print on the label, signifying wines 'produced and bottled by prestigious winemakers' in Chile, to distinguish it from even cheaper bottles; 13.5% alcohol.

FRANCE

🍷 8 Côtes du Rhône 2015 £3.99

Cherry-coloured and bright, a healthy gently spicy wine bright in flavour too. Miles better than its counterpart Côtes du Rhône Villages.

ITALY

🍷 7 Corte Alle Mura Chianti 2015 £4.49

Inoffensive cherry-fruit perfectly wholesome unChianti-like pasta red at, redemptively, an unChianti-like price.

🍷 9 Fortezza dei Colli Chianti Classico 2014 £6.99

Relishable full-fruit proper Chianti with the right lifted flavours, plump heft and authentic nutskin finish; a long-serving, realistically-priced regular on Lidl's core list and a very dependable one.

🍷 7 Barolo 2012 £9.99

This Lidl perennial has a curious distinction: it comes in a claret-shaped bottle instead of the burgundy-type otherwise favoured for this noble DOCG. This one is certainly authentic with the right limpid ruby colour, but kicks off with a curiously stewed nose. I was tasting it at home so had time to let this pong disperse, revealing a friendly sleek-cherry recognisable fruit; 14% alcohol.

RED WINES

PORTUGAL

⚜ 8 **Azinhaga de Ouro Douro Reserva 2015**   £5.99
An inky-dark and interesting Port-country red with
hints of the fortified wine's spice and fire, plus a lick of
marzipan in the depths of the rounded blackcurrant fruit;
easy to like and 13.5% alcohol.

SPAIN

⚜ 8 **Baturrica Gran Reserva 2010**   £4.99
Mature but still quite tough middleweight Tarragona
blend of Tempranillo and Cabernet Sauvignon gives an
expectedly blackcurranty fruit that will nicely match
spicy-meaty menus such as chilli con carne; cheap for an
antique.

⚜ 8 **Cepa Lebrel Rioja Reserva 2012**   £5.49
It's a lightweight, but delivers good blackcurrant-and-
vanilla character at a low price for Rioja Reserva.

WHITE WINES

CHILE

⚜ 8 **Cimarosa Pedro Jimenez 2015**   £3.99
Wild lemon-melon-spicy aroma from this Andean
curiosity is followed up by dry, amost bracing, tangy
corresponding fruit that reminded me of Austria's
Gruner Veltliner (currently quite in vogue). The Pedro
Jimenez, known as Ximenes or PX at home in Spain is
the sweetening grape for dark, rich sherries; here it's in a
very different role, and a commendable one.

FRANCE

⚜ 8 **Chablis 2015**   £8.99
Fine mineral wine; has nice flinty rasp alongside the
sweetly ripe Chardonnay fruit. Soft Chablis rather than
the steely kind.

WHITE WINES

ITALY

9 Montejanu Vermentino di Sardegna 2015   **£4.99**
Sardinia's signature white grape on cracking form in this cheap and thoroughly cheerful fresh-lush dry white with textbook grapefruit lift to aroma and flavour and a nice blanched-almond creaminess to the body – a bargain.

8 Gavi 2016   **£5.49**
Nice colour and notes of grapefruit on the nose of this plump Piedmont wine lead to dry but luxuriant flavours; distinctive and a nifty match for spicier dishes as well as Italian menus.

N. ZEALAND

9 Cimarosa New Zealand Sauvignon Blanc 2016   **£5.89**
Immediate hit of tangy crisp gooseberry fruit gets this shining Marlborough Sauvignon off to an impressive start, followed up by plenty of grassy green freshness and good lingering flavours; convincing effects and remarkable value.

SOUTH AFRICA

10 Cimarosa South African Chenin Blanc 2016   **£3.89**
I am top-scoring this because for the money it's fantastically good – fresh, wholesome dry everyday wine with an elderflower whiff, meadow-sweet white fruit, trademark honey trace of Chenin Blanc and clean edge. The thing is, I wonder who buys this? How many shoppers really do know that in the Cape they make great wines from the Chenin Blanc? This wine deserves maximum attention and not just because it's fantastically cheap.

WHITE WINES

SPAIN

🍷 8 **Visigodo Rueda Blanco 2015**   £4.99
Nicely made Verdejo-Viura blend from estimable Rueda
region, crisply dry with a grassy lushness.

🍷 7 **Cepa Lebrel Rioja Blanco 2016**   £4.99
Recognisable example of rather overlooked wine style;
generously coloured, cheerfully sweet-pear-scented and
plump with peach and apricot fruits; simple and cheap.

SPARKLING WINES

FRANCE

🍷 8 **Crémant de Bourgogne Brut**   £7.49
Soft, gently foaming Chardonnay fizz of easy charm and
edged with a lifting citrus acidity; good value.

🍷 8 **Champagne Comte de Senneval Brut**   £9.99
This is incredibly cheap and not at all bad: recognisable
bakery aroma, busily fizzy, lively appley-lemony fruit;
yup, it's champagne. I've invested in a couple of bottles
intending to keep them a year or two to see if the contents
develop. Watch this space for future reports.

Majestic

 Yes, I know. Majestic is not a supermarket. But it's a major player. The range of wines, at about 1,250, is more than any of the supermarkets have to offer. There are 210 of the 'warehouse' outlets throughout the nation. In case you didn't already know, there is now no minimum purchase in the stores or online, and the home-delivery operation has in the last year been whizzed up to offer a named-day service, including next day if you want it.

Although the wholesale approach has been dropped, Majestic still operates a perpetual multibuy policy. The published prices are universally in pairs: one for purchase of five or fewer bottles at a time; one for six or more, any mix. The Mix Six prices are typically 10 to 20 per cent lower. In the following pages therefore, you'll find every wine comes with a single-bottle price first and the mixed-six price second.

These prices apply equally in store and online, and on many individual wines there will be additional promotions through the year. It can seem complicated, but there are always some good deals.

The Majestic range was once rather predictable; they stuck with a lot of the same suppliers year after year, many of them extremely good. Now, many of my old favourites have been eliminated; emphasis has altered. But there are still great numbers of great wines – including 400 or so 'fine' wines, thus elevated by prices above £20.

And there are own-label wines too. The first range of these, artfully called Definition, came in a couple of years ago, and they are proving good, on the whole. More recently introduced is a 'Majestic Loves' range of 'entry level' wines at under £6. I tasted these for the first time in 2017. None appears among my recommendations in this edition. I believe Majestic is stronger towards the mid-price level. I don't believe it is ready to compete with the major supermarkets in this very competitive sector.

RED WINES

AUSTRALIA

🍷 8 **The Astronomer Shiraz 2015** £6.99/5.99
Another starry vintage for this 'entry-level' wine from
excellent Victoria outfit De Bortoli. Bouncing blackberry
fruit with gentle spice and mint; 14% alcohol.

🍷 8 **La La Land Tempranillo 2015** £9.99/£7.99
The name might not win any Oscars, but this Murray
Darling (Victoria) varietal has juicy blackcurrant ripeness
(but not overripeness) and wholesome balance; 13.5%
alcohol.

🍷 8 **Definition Shiraz 2016** £12.99/£10.99
Deep purple young wine has masses of upfront liquorous
sweetly brambly fruit in ideal balance; lush natural-
tasting food red (roast lamb) of easy charm; 14% alcohol.

FRANCE

🍷 8 **Olivier Dubois Pinot Noir 2016** £8.99/£7.99
Generic wine from the south (not Burgundy) has the juicy
wholesome brightness of Pinot fruit; I've written 'wheaty'
which means I liked it without entirely knowing why.

🍷 9 **Domaine Les Yeuses Les Epices
Syrah 2014** £9.99/£8.99
Red-meat Pays d'Oc has liquorice darkness at the centre
of its spicy-juicy blackberry fruit; from pungent brambly
nose to lipsmacking grippy finish, a delicious and
satisfying winter red; 13.5% alcohol.

🍷 9 **Definition Côtes du Rhône 2015** £10.99/£8.99
My pick of the Definition own-label range this year, a
sumptuously ripe (14.5% alcohol) and spicy rounded
wine for hearty food matches – winter cassoulet, game
stews.

RED WINES

FRANCE

8 **Definition Beaujolais Villages 2014** £10.99/£8.99
Impressively expensive for a mere village wine, but this is really good, with defined juicy, almost crunchy, purple-tasting fruit in the best Beaujolais manner; the 2014 as tasted was delicious, but I guess the 2015 will succeed soon enough – should be another good one.

8 **Château Côtes de Blaignan 2012** £12.99/£10.99
Jolly dense and grippy claret (Médoc) with dark toasty cassis fruit all in a sleek, developed frame of flavour; nice buy.

9 **Château Caronne**
Ste-Gemme 2012 £15.99/£13.99
Familiar Haut-Médoc Cru Bourgeois estate which seems amazingly consistent over the years in quality and fairness in price. This maturing vintage offers a fine violet and cedar perfume, plump, ripe and intense blackcurrant fruit nicely evolved and elegant in weight and balance. Serious claret.

8 **Santenay Louis Latour 2014** £21.99/£17.49
From one of the humbler Beaune appellations, this bright and edgy cherry-raspberry burgundy has juicy charm and contemplative depths; Latour is a good merchant, and the discounted price is almost reasonable.

ITALY

8 **Carlino Rosso 2016** £5.99/£4.99
Easy-drinking Sicilian pasta red at an affordable price; sunny-ripe fruit and clean dry finish.

8 **Copertino Masseria Monaci 2012** £9.99/£8.99
Copertino is neighbour to Salice Salentino (see next entry) and makes red wines from Negroamaro grapes that seem to me to have a volcanic savour, dark, piquant and toothsome with plummy bite; this fits the profile nicely.

RED WINES

**9 Salice Salentino Vereto Agricole
Vallone 2013**   £11.99/£9.99
Gripping Puglian Negroamaro; has the characteristic
savoury astringency imparted by the grapes' thick skins
with accompanying darkness of spicy fruit enriched by
notions of eucalyptus; delicious, earthy distinctive red to
match game and roasts.

8 Definition Chianti Classico 2013   £12.99/£10.99
Immediately convincing Chianti style, beguiling ripe
cherry-plum fruits, developed and sleek with keen
nutskin-dry finish; 13.5% alcohol.

**8 Lay & Wheeler Brunello di
Montalcino 2011**   £32.00/£27.00
Lay & Wheeler is a dynastic Colchester wine merchant
Majestic bought a while ago, and Brunello is a sort
of super-Chianti made at the ancient hilltown of
Montalcino. This one is gorgeous, replete with cassis/
coffee/creamy lushness in sublime balance, tasting every
bit as extravagant as its price; 14.5% alcohol.

10 Porta 6 Lisboa 2015   £8.99/£7.99
Lovely pruny-cinnamon black-fruit nose on this slinky
classic Lisbon red from proper indigenous Portuguese
grape varieties; you get sweet violets, cloves and fruits-of-
the-forest flavours at its dark centre and perfectly pitched
dry finish to the whole performance; 13.5% alcohol.
Great food matcher – anything from saucy fish stews to
sausages and mash.

ITALY

PORTUGAL

RED WINES

8 Finca Carelio 2014 £9.99/£7.99
Chunky Tempranillo (the Rioja grape) from the Toro, a region renowned for its sinewy reds, this is generous with cassis intensity and well-defined by its tannin; 14.5% alcohol.

9 Papa Luna Calatayud 2013 £9.99/£8.99
Big baked-fruit intense dark chocolate monster has taut enjoyably bitter frame to the flavour; spicy-food matcher with plenty of woof; 13.5% alcohol. Good value.

8 Matsu El Picaro Toro 2016 £9.99/£8.99
Arresting photographic label featuring a young man in a tweedy flat cap is not let down by the well-knit dark blackcurranty fruit in this substantial Toro red with plenty of whoomph and grip; 14.5% alcohol.

9 Lay & Wheeler Rioja Gran Reserva 2008 £30.00/£25.00
Never mind the price, this is a must-try wine of true distinction. Sumptuous, browning-at-the-edge ruby colour, wildly intoxicating cassis-vanilla nose and the silkiest, purist perfectly developed Rioja fruit, ideally poised and 13.5% alcohol. Lay & Wheeler is Majestic's fine-wine arm, and the wine is made by Viña Holtonia in the Rioja Alta.

8 Edna Valley Pinot Noir 2014 £14.99/£9.99
Sunny Californian pure varietal has friendly plumpness of cherry-raspberry fruit and looks decent value at the mix-six price; 14% alcohol.

SPAIN

USA

Majestic

PINK WINES

🍷 8 Louison Rosé Côteaux d'Aix en Provence 2016 £9.99/£8.99

Gleefully lurid colour and brightness of perky strawberry fruit too in this fresh and likeable dry wine.

FRANCE

🍷 7 Definition Rosé 2016 £11.99/£9.99

It's a delicate-looking thing from Provence, pale shell-pink, with a rose-petal nose and more red fruit than you might expect, briskly balanced; dry, fresh, pricey.

🍷 8 Black Cottage Rosé 2016 £12.99/£10.99

Marlborough Pinot Noir pink might well be inspired by the rosé style of Sancerre, pale, crisp and cold-river-pebble fresh. This certainly stood out from the crowd and just about merits its price.

N. ZEALAND

WHITE WINES

🍷 8 Zuccardi Chardonnay 2014 £11.99/£7.99

Maturing creamily-oaked and sweetly ripe Tupungato wine cleverly balanced with minerality and citrus lift; 13.5% alcohol. Note the generous mix-six discount.

ARGENTINA

🍷 9 Morandé One to One Gewürztraminer 2016 £8.99/£6.99

Bold lychee perfume and crisp spicy fruit in this well-contrived spin on the original Alsace theme are trimmed up with a fine citrus twist to make a very distinctive aperitif, or an assertive match for Asian menus; good value.

CHILE

WHITE WINES

CHILE

🍷 8 **Luis Felipe Edwards Gran Reserva
Chardonnay 2016** £9.99/£7.99
Golden colour and a big whack of melon-peach-sweet
apple fruit in this coconut-oaked but fresh and healthily
balanced Casablanca Valley food white.

🍷 8 **Santa Ema Sauvignon Gris 2016** £9.99/£7.99
Ripe Leyda Valley wine has clear asparagus notes atop
the grassy Sauvignon sapidity – the Gris strain of the
variety contributing some smoky complexity – and long,
lush flavours; 13.5% alcohol.

🍷 8 **Symbiose Piquepoul Sauvignon Blanc Cuvée
Florence Côtes de Thau 2015** £8.99/£7.99
Symbiotic or cynical exploitation? The Côtes de Thau is
neighbour to fashionable Picpoul de Pinet in Mediterranean
France and clearly anxious to cash in. This crafty blend has
a nice saline-green-grassy style that works well.

🍷 8 **Villemarin Picpoul de Pinet 2016** £9.99/£7.99
Plenty of colour and flavour interest in this ripe but
refreshingly green orchardy spin on the popular Picpoul
style. Ace seafood match with a good twang.

🍷 8 **Kuhlmann-Platz Cave de Hunawihr
Riesling 2016** £11.99/£9.99
Tangy-limey Alsace dry wine with minerality and long
racy fruit.

🍷 9 **Domaine Jomain Bourgogne
Chardonnay 2014** £15.99/£13.99
Barrel-fermented green-gold assertively lush and
minerally generic burgundy from vineyards neighbouring
Puligny-Montrachet, no less. I was suitably impressed.

WHITE WINES

Majestic

FRANCE

10 Domaines Schlumberger Grand Cru
Pinot Gris 2013 £17.99/£15.99

A spectacular Alsace wine of opulent colour giving off Sauternes-like aromas of honey and tropical fruit, smoky and exotic in its long flavours exactly as Pinot Gris from a grand cru site should be and with a perfectly pitched acidity and 13.5% alcohol. This is a rare wine that Alsace devotees should seriously consider – the price seems very fair indeed.

9 St-Aubin 1er Cru Domaine Gérard
Thomas et Filles 2015 £29.99/£25.99

Stony-peachy and butter-luscious oaked Chardonnay from one of Burgundy's true-value appellations, neighbour to Chassagne-Montrachet. Very nifty balance between richness and freshness here and a safe investment for the right occasion – scallops or lobster come easily to mind.

ITALY

8 Carlino Bianco 2016 £5.99/£4.99

Sicilian dry everyday white is at a new low-price at Majestic and welcome both for its economy and delicate floral charm.

7 Definition Pinot Grigio 2016 £9.99/£8.99

Nice enough Friuli wine; tangy dry but with a hint or two of PG smoke and spice; price seems a little high.

WHITE WINES

9 Russian Jack Sauvignon Blanc 2016 £10.99/£8.24

NEW ZEALAND

Retro-Soviet-style label but a very now and very delicious Sauvignon by admirable Martinborough Vineyards with a stimulating attack of zesty grassy-nettly fruit, deep intense gooseberry, crisp green flavours and a textbook lemon-lime acidity to finish. Russian Jack was a merchant seaman from, er, Latvia, who made his name in the Kiwi wine business.

7 Casal de Ventozela Vinho Verde 2015 £8.99/£7.99

PORTUGAL

This didn't taste much like vinho verde, the 'green wine' so-called because it's customarily made from half-ripened grapes to make the tart and eye-watering wines (mostly red) relished by oily-sardine-scoffing Portuguese drinkers, as it is sweetened for the pap-eating UK market. Where was I? Oh yes. Liked this perky variation just for itself.

8 Diemersdal Sauvignon Blanc 2017 £11.99/£8.99

S. AFRICA

Brisk and business-like grassy-nettly Sauvignon in what might be called the better Kiwi style; impressively vivid and direct.

8 Viña Albali Verdejo Rueda 2016 £7.99/£6.99

SPAIN

Viña Albali is fondly known for its bargain Rioja-style reds from La Mancha, and here they are having a go at the white-wine equivalent from Rueda, except this really is from Rueda, and tastes exactly as you would hope: crisp, tangy and brimming with grassy fruit, and all at a sensible-enough price.

WHITE WINES

8 Nettie Viognier McManis 2015   £8.99/£7.99
Limpid but lively exotically perfumed California varietal shows peach and apricot ripeness and finishes brisk; 13.5% alcohol.

8 Au Bon Climat Chardonnay 2015 £27.99/£22.99
This celebrated Santa Barbara winery is on good form with this toasty, richly yellow-tasting sunny Californian deluxe varietal for a grand occasion (including Thanksgiving turkey); invest with confidence; 13.5% alcohol.

—Marks & Spencer—

Are M&S wines expensive? I am sure plenty of shoppers believe so. It might be down to the inevitable association with the legendary food range. It may or may not be expensive for what it is, but price isn't the primary attraction.

Tasting my way through more than a hundred M&S wines on a very well-spent day this year I was reminded, as I always am, just how consistently fascinating, varied and delicious the range is. I was giving high scores to wine after wine priced at £10 and above. I am parsimonious about points for pricier wines, but felt no cause for hesitation.

Later, transcribing my notes, something dawned. The prices noted were for the wines in store. If you buy them online by the six-bottle case, which is how the M&S wine website operates, you'll probably get them for less. Most of the time, as far as I can tell, online wine shoppers are offered 25 per cent off all cases for orders of two or more. It's not a permanent offer, but it seems remarkably consistent.

So, take one of my top M&S buys this year, Langhe Nebbiolo 2015 at £11.00. I've scored it 10 because to my way of thinking it's perfect. Now I realize I can buy six bottles of it for it £49.50, or £8.25 each. What do I score it now? I don't even think about it. Just order a case straight away, plus another favourite to qualify my order, and they're delivered pronto, and free.

In the interests of balance I must report that M&S still do a very decent range of wines well under £10. The new 2016 vintage of perennial dry white Gers at £5.50 is terrific and the House Rosé 2016 from the Midi at £5.00 is my best-value pink wine of the year.

Upscale a bit, M&S have gone into the Bordeaux 'en primeur' business, buying posh clarets before they are even bottled then offering them at what I assume are advantageous prices as soon as they are delivered. They have launched with the 2014 vintage, a fairly ordinary one but arguably as good as anything since 2010, and the wines seem pretty good though not forward enough to drink now. I loved the Château d'Angludet at £27.00 and thought the two *grands crus classés*, Grand Puy Lacoste and Rauzan-Ségla, no better at £65.00.

I must mention a new wine called Litmus Pinot Noir 2014. It's something like a very wholesome red burgundy and the £30.00 price tag doesn't seem outrageous. The real surprise is its origins. It's from the Denbies wine estate at Dorking, Surrey.

RED WINES

AUSTRALIA

 8 **Margaret River Cabernet Sauvignon 2015 £11.00**
Purple briary-bright Cabernet by the formidable Evans
and Tate winery has been long oak-barrel-aged giving
a somewhat claret-like sleekness, but there's plenty of
exuberant ripeness here too; 14% alcohol.

 8 **Pure South Pinot Noir 2016   £15.00**
Pale pigeon-eye colour to this Tasmanian pure varietal
leads into an almost delicate cherry fruit, but with a
backbone; sleek and long, scrummy Pinot with some oak
fortification; 13.5% alcohol.

CHILE

 8 **CM Carmenère Elqui 2016   £8.50**
Nice expression of the Carmenère grape grown in Chile's
most northern vineyard region, the Elqui Valley, is
sweetly ripe with blackberry juiciness and plump weight
in the best Chilean tradition; 14% alcohol. Grilled steak
will suit.

 9 **Los Molles Syrah 2014   £11.00**
The colour is close to black, and the intensity of the
fruit takes up the theme — spicy dark flavours in a silky
medium (aged in oak casks) and well-judged weight
finishing taut and trim; 14% alcohol. Exciting food red –
roast venison and rabbit leap to mind.

ENGLAND

 9 **Litmus Pinot Noir 2014   £30.00**
This is something like a jolly wholesome village red
burgundy, but it is in fact a product of the Denbies Estate
in Dorking, Surrey. The grapes were clearly brilliantly
ripe and healthy at harvest and were fermented in oak
barrels, some new. It's terrifically good and terrifically
expensive. Only in 10 stores so try online.

RED WINES

🍷 8 Domaine de Brignac 2016   £5.75
Bright and juicy picnic red from the Hérault has cherry-raspberry fruit with a suggestion of marzipan sweetness; 11.5% alcohol.

🍷 9 Corbières Domaine Combe du Buis 2015   £8.50
Reds from the Languedoc appellation of Corbières can be a bit overheated and coarse but this is a smoothie, with heft and ripeness as well as black fruits and spice, slicked up with some crafty oak contact; agreeably plausible.

🍷 8 Château Gillet 2015   £8.50
This firm generic Bordeaux is ripe and already rounding out to make savoury blackcurranty drinking; safe bet.

🍷 9 Henry Fessy Coteaux Bourguignons 2016   £9.50
This is a burgundy-Beaujolais, made by leading Beaujolais producer Fessy from Gamay grapes. It's terrific, purple, juicy and bouncing, but with integrity and heft, vinified traditionally rather than by the Beaujolais method of carbonic maceration.

🍷 9 Plessis-Duval Saumur Champigny 2015   £10.00
Crunchy-stalky brightly purple Loire Cabernet Franc, bursting with vigorous red fruits, a proper standout food wine (anything that needs 'cutting' by crisp red flavours) with intensity, weight and leafy loveliness. Loire reds such as this chill very nicely.

🍷 8 Pont du Gard Red 2016   £10.00
The sublime golden-stone Roman aqueduct in the Languedoc gives its name to the local IGT under which this well-built Merlot-Syrah blend is made; ripe black cherry fruits and spicy-silky blackberry ripeness stream juicily together; 14% alcohol.

RED WINES

9 Lirac Les Closiers 2015   £10.50

Cursed with the soubriquet 'poor man's Châteauneuf du Pape' this neighbour of the famed Rhône AOP can come pretty close; this is sleek and rich with pruny pomegranate spicy dark, dark fruits of enticing complexity and endurance; great stuff; 14% alcohol.

8 Fleurie 2016   £11.50

Violets and raspberries on the nose of this senior Beaujolais cru assure a deliciously juicy run of fruit flavours in silky context.

9 Domaine de la Curnière Vacqueyras 2015 £13.50

Whopping tarry Rhône village wine, liquoricey and lavish with a fine grippy outer carapace to the spicy black-fruit and all in elegant, flowing balance; unoaked wine, lovely now and will develop; 14.5% alcohol.

9 Château d'Angludet 2014   £27.00

Inky-dark young Margaux from M&S's en-primeur-2014 claret offering is already sumptuous with intense cassis-coffee-cedar aromas and fruits, quite gorgeously ripe and full. It's a wine to keep years longer and at this price a sound investment. Just 80 stores or online.

8 Château Chasse Spleen 2014   £33.00

From the celebrated Moulis (Médoc) estate said to have been renamed when visitor Lord Byron declared the wine 'chases away my spleen', this has dense colour, big black cherry/cassis grand claret aroma and fat, new-oak fruit just coming round. Needs time, but buy now as this is a fine-wine parcel and will sell out; 13.5% alcohol. In 80 stores or online.

FRANCE

RED WINES

ITALY

🍷 8 **Puglia Rosso 2016**   £7.50
Crisply clean dark-brambly Negroamaro of bright
juiciness and middling weight makes a pleasing pasta
match.

🍷 8 **Montepulciano d'Abruzzo 2016**   £8.00
These Adriatic hedgerow reds can be pale and dilute but
this has substance and keen acidity giving it the proper
juicy refreshing quality.

🍷 10 **Langhe Nebbiolo 2015**   £11.00
The Nebbiolo wines of Piedmont – Barolo, Barbaresco
and generic Langhe – form one of Italy's spiffiest wine
styles. But they can be awfully expensive. This one by
local jumbo producer Araldica illustrates the method
with its jewel-like ruby colour, sweet cherry-coffee-rose-
petal nose, silky but intense sappy redcurrant fruit and
austere grippy finish. Fine and elegant, and cheap for
what it is; 14% alcohol.

🍷 8 **Chianti Classico Riserva Castello
della Paneretta 2013**   £13.50
Grand chianti going a nice orange at the colour's edge
has had two years in oak casks and runs silky-plummy-
cherry-cassis-richness over the tongue with a textbook
nutskin dry finish; just the match for vitello, even bistecca
fiorentina; 13.5% alcohol.

N. ZEALAND

🍷 8 **Craft 3 Pinot Noir 2016**   £13.00
Fine edgy Marlborough wine, sleek and concentrated
with that keynote Kiwi minty lift to the cherry-raspberry
fruit; good heft and balance.

RED WINES

N. ZEALAND

🍷 8 **Crossroads Syrah 2014**   £33.00
An M&S fine wine I noted as 'Kiwi Crozes Hermitage or even Kiwi Hermitage' in deference to the two great Syrah appellations of the northern Rhône. Of course this Hawkes Bay prodigy has its own merits, silkiness, dark gentle spiciness and so on; certainly a find; 13.5% alcohol.

SOUTH AFRICA

🍷 9 **Helderberg Cellars Cabernet Sauvignon 2015**   £10.00
Dense colour with a roasty blackcurranty gamey nose, the fruit is silky and expensively plump, cushiony even, and in artful balance with the taut acidity; it's a wine that grows on you, more than earning its price, and offering more clear evidence that Cape winemakers are seriously upping their game; 14.5% alcohol.

SPAIN

🍷 9 **Las Falleras Tinto 2016**   £5.00
The bright crimson-purple colour of this wholesome Valencian red is a good clue to its easy berry ripeness, held together by friendly tannin; really well-made wine at a true bargain price.

🍷 8 **Tapa Roja Old Vines 2015**   £9.00
Roja, not Rioja, please note. This is a dark elderberry-raisiny hearty winter red from the bucolic Mediterranean DO of Yecla (long way from Rioja) and a good one, big and darkly satisfying, a match for spicy and chilli dishes; 14.5% alcohol.

🍷 8 **Sinols Negre 2016**   £11.00
From the Emporda DO of Spain's far northeastern frontier a luminous, intense blend entirely of French grape varieties Grenache, Carignan, Cabernet Sauvignon, Merlot and Syrah. You get buckets of ripe, savoury berry fruits, rounded but grippy; huge meaty red with 14.5% alcohol. Not for wimps.

RED WINES

TURKEY

🍷 8 **Anfora Trio 2015** £9.50

Save Turkey: Try the Wine. This is mostly Cabernet Sauvignon and Syrah, with local grape Kalecik Karasi. Good defined black fruit flavours, you wouldn't guess it came from anywhere odd; 14% alcohol.

PINK WINES

ARGENTINA

🍷 8 **Beach House Rosé 2016** £6.00

The grapes, mostly Syrah and Tempranillo, are grown 1000 metres up in the Andes, which makes a nonsense of the littoral nomenclature, but you do get a certain mountain-air clarity in the red summer fruit; dry, crisp and pink-tasting and cheap. Don't let the naff label deter you.

FRANCE

🍷 9 **House Rosé 2016** £5.00

I have just noticed that M&S rosés now come in clear glass. They used to be bottled in green, to preserve the colour, but this probably inhibited sales. The colour's a big selling point. But times change. This Toulouse wine is very pale but by no means wan: bouncing ripe red soft summer fruits, fresh and stimulating, and cheap. Rosé as it should be.

WHITE WINES

ARGENTINA

🍷 9 **Fisherman's Catch Chenin Blanc 2016** £7.00

This cleverly construed Mendoza dry white has exotic fleeting-honeysuckle perfume, and positively racy fresh citrus-finishing lush orchard fruit. Very nice wine keenly priced. Don't be put off by the clunky 70s-style typographic label.

WHITE WINES

10 Craft 3 Adelaide Hills Chardonnay 2016   £10.00
Not just Aussie Chardonnay, this is M&S Aussie Chardonnay. It is perfectly pitched between luscious peachy ripeness, luxed up by partial fermentation in new oak, and trim, fresh acidity; 13.5% alcohol. To me the very manifestation of what Oz Chardy should be. The price looks low. Craft 3 is an M&S brand for a number of New World wines made jointly by the producers and the M&S winemakers – originally, if I remember, a team of three.

9 Barossa Viognier 2016   £10.00
M&S winemaker Belinda Kleinig concedes that the Viognier grape is 'vehemently loved by some and really not loved by others' but urges us all to try this one, made with Yalumba, a Barossa Valley winery founded in 1849 by a Dorset brewer called Samuel Smith. Good on him, because this is a great Viognier, gilded in colour and exotic succulent flavours all trimmed with citrus to a fine dry edge.

9 Hunter Semillon 2016   £13.00
Tropical flavours lead here, with pineapple and banana coming first to mind in an aroma that closely evokes the ambrosia of Sauternes (in which Semillon plays a major role) but this is a 'dry' wine and yes, fresh as a daisy, contrived in exemplary balance and equally at home as an aperitif or a partner to shellfish, tricky salads or rice dishes; 11.5% alcohol. Made by Tyrells. In only 100 stores or try online.

8 Tierra y Hombre Sauvignon Blanc 2016   £8.50
Casablanca Valley perennial on shining form in this crisp and grassy vintage with a long-lingering asparagus-tinged fruit.

AUSTRALIA

CHILE

WHITE WINES

Marks & Spencer

ENGLAND

🍷 8 **Urban Foxes Bacchus 2015**   £13.50
Muscatty but poised and pleasingly balanced in spite of
the irritating name; characterful aperitif wine from Kent
for patriotric drinkers; 11% alcohol.

FRANCE

🍷 9 **Gers 2016**   £5.50
Gascon perennial from stalwart co-operative Plaimont
Producteurs on fresh, perky form in this new vintage,
bristling with sunny-ripe white fruits; 11.5% alcohol.
M&S doesn't specialise in cheap wines, and this one is an
outstanding bargain.

🍷 8 **Le Fleuve Bleu Blanc 2016**   £6.00
Attractive sailboat label for this alluring seaside-fresh
Languedoc dry Grenache Blanc is citrus-tangy without
sharpness.

🍷 8 **Picpoul de Pinet 2016**   £9.50
On-trend Mediterranean seafood dry white with more
colour than most and possibly more intensity of briny
white orchard fruit too; stands out from the crowd.

🍷 8 **Bourgogne Chardonnay 2016**   £10.00
Vivid crisp Chalonnais Chardonnay with an extra
dimension of richness perhaps imparted by the 1% of
the wine that has been barrel-aged; fine young white
burgundy for seafood occasions and posh parties.

🍷 8 **Domaine Jacky Marteau Touraine
Sauvignon Blanc 2016**   £10.00
Keen green Loire runs deep in its grassy-nettly flavours;
Touraine is definitely the name to look for if you like your
Sauvignon clearly defined and crisp.

WHITE WINES

🍷 8   **Petit Chablis 2016**   £11.00
The appellation Petit Chablis covers vineyards on the periphery of the famous Burgundy outpost's domain, but does produce some decent wines. This has the right green-gold colour and steeliness of crisp Chardonnay fruit – it's proper Chablis.

🍷 8   **Chablis 2014**   £12.05
The comfortingly familiar label style doesn't seem to have changed in decades, and the wine is unchangingly dependable too; finely coloured mineral and ripe, leesy wine of authentic character.

🍷 9   **Mâcon-Villages La Roche Vineuse 2015**   £14.00
Straw-gold precocious peachy Chardonnay, unoaked but of portentous weight and intensity; it's mellow and luscious beyond its years and not overpriced (for burgundy). Only 172 stores; try online.

🍷 9   **Chablis Brocard Vieilles Vignes 2015**   £16.00
The rich colour is reassuringly shot with the green tinge for which Chablis is renowned, and there's a lushness to the ripe apple fruit that might owe something to oak contact as well as the sunniness of the vintage; good flintiness here too.

🍷 8   **Chablis Brocard Grand Cru Les
          Preuses 2007**   £44.00
Millionaire's wine a decade old; pure-gold colour, a glorious spirity sweet-stone-fruit nose and luscious, even buttery ripe, oaked Chardonnay fruits with the steely Chablis minerality and citrus acidity to balance; superb rare wine at a rare price. In only 20 stores; try online.

FRANCE

WHITE WINES

9 Atlantis Santorini 2015 £12.00

Santorini, Aegean island paradise and site of the great volcanic eruption of 1500 BC that wiped out the Minoans, makes fascinating dry white wines from Assyrtiko grapes: this is sleekly sapid with a fleeting salinity to the fresh white fruits, suggesting the volcanic nature of the soil and evoking the hot sea breezes that lure devoted travellers; great stuff.

8 Terre Siciliane Bianco 2016 £7.00

Sunny island blend of local varieties Grillo, Catarratto and Inzolia carries a lick of heather honey through the crisp, dry course of the flavours.

9 Falanghina Beneventano 2016 £7.50

Big colour and dollops of peachy-melony ripeness in this nonetheless briskly bright and fresh Campania dry wine for matching with creamy pasta, charcuterie and even salads as well as fish and poultry.

8 Gavi Quadro Sei 2016 £9.00

Gavi, the once chi-chi nutty-lush dry white of Piedmont seems a bit common or garden now, but this one by regional giant Araldica does honour to the name: full orchard-fruit effect with a real glow of ripeness and neat citrus edge.

8 La Prendina Estate Pinot Grigio 2016 £10.50

Closer to the Alsace Pinot Gris style than the bog-standard Veneto slop, this Mantuan dry wine has discreet smoke, spice and weight of ripeness to set it apart.

WHITE WINES

ITALY

9 **Ascheri Langhe Arneis 2016** £13.50
An M&S star wine from the misty slopes of Piedmont's
Langhe, this is excitingly steely and bright on the one
hand and lavishly generous with the ripe apple fruit on
the other; it's unoaked but somehow creamy and rich. A
delectable contrivance that would go awfully well with
scallops.

N. ZEALAND

10 **Seifried Grüner Veltliner 2016** £11.00
Estimable Seifried Estate's take on the Austrian original is
quite faithful – I wouldn't guess this is a Kiwi wine – with
the right delicate crisp-pear, grapefruit and spice style,
dry and marked by a characteristic gentle white-pepper
asperity; real fascinator and a fine match for charcuterie
as well as fish.

PORTUGAL

7 **Tapada de Villar Vinho Verde 2016** £9.00
Less sweetened than some, and a pleasant delicate
elderflower freshness with the faintest spritz; 10.5%
alcohol.

SOUTH AFRICA

8 **Dolphin Bay Chardonnay 2016** £6.00
Good-value dry party wine showing peachy ripeness
and sweet-apple freshness enriched with some crafty oak
contact.

8 **Ken Forrester Workhorse Chenin
Blanc 2016** £8.50
I do like the industrious-looking horse on the label of this
handsomely coloured and thoroughly three-dimensional
Stellenbosch dry wine. Nectar-hinting nose, good rush of
bright white fruit, tangy acidity.

WHITE WINES

SOUTH AFRICA

9 Bohoek Semillon 2016   £10.00
Pineapple, nectarine and a pungent tinge of lemon
verbena all crop up among the aromas and flavours of
this lovely ripe, carefully oaked dry white with a 15%
Sauvignon Blanc addition; long, nuanced and thought-
provoking food wine – suits all kinds of fowl as well as
fish and creamily sauced recipes.

SPAIN

8 Las Falleras White 2016   £5.00
This dependable Valencian dry party wine from Viura
grape (of Rioja Blanca fame) is fresh and wholesome;
11.5% alcohol.

8 Jordi Miró Garnacha Blanca 2016   £9.50
Mediterranean dry wine (DO Terra Alta) has bounteous
apple-and-pear fruit with weight as well as poise; ripe and
satisfying and 13.5% alcohol. Drink with white meats as
well as fishy dishes.

8 Val de Souto 2016   £12.00
Mystery dry white from the Ribeiro DO in Galicia, very
much modern Spanish – racy almost Sauvignon-like (but
mostly from indigenous Treixadura grape), brimming
with tangy freshness, yet contemplatively complex and
leesy; fascinating.

USA

8 New York White 2016   £9.00
Curious mélange of Seyval Blanc, Riesling and Sauvignon
Blanc from the Finger Lakes where the towns have names
like Geneva and Dundee, makes an aromatic dry white-
fruit of more than curiosity value.

SPARKLING WINES

8 **Lyme Bay Classic Cuvee 2013**   £20.00
Tangy citrus edge to the recognisable champagne grape mix (four parts Pinot Noir, one part Chardonnay), this Devon single-vintage sparkler is convincing and reasonably priced. Sold in only 10 stores so look online.

9 **English Sparkling Reserve Brut**   £22.00
From Kent's Chapel Down winery – destined one day perhaps to be the Moët & Chandon of English fizz – a fine yeasty, generous sparkler mainly from Chardonnay and Pinot Noir already mellow although of recent (2014) harvest; should develop further but already delicious. Realistically priced.

9 **Digby Fine English Leander Pink**   £30.00
A 'negociant' wine – Digby Fine English, address 1 Berkeley Square, London buys in its grapes from partner vineyards across England – this is very discreetly pink and delicately strawberry in its fruit, inviting and mellow, with a nice citrus twang. It is much in the champagne style (Pinots and Chardonnay from Kent, Sussex and Hampshire) and really quite special in its own right. Only in 43 stores so try online.

8 **Crémant de Bourgogne Les Caves
de Hautes Côtes Brut**   £12.00
This creamily foaming, yeasty-orchardy sparkling burgundy is mostly Pinot Noir, with floral perfume and plenty of crisp refreshment.

ENGLAND

FRANCE

SPARKLING WINES

🍷 8 Oudinot Medium Dry Rosé £29.00

House pink champagne Oudinot Rosé is brisk fun, but this richer version is a blast. It has four times the 'dosage' of sugar at disgorgement but is a more subtle step-up in sweetness than that. Salmon colour, ripe strawberry perfume and fruit, thrillingly balanced flow of flavours and finish; a truly artful crowd-pleaser champagne – at a price.

🍷 8 Masottina Bellante £10.00

Pink and frothy generic northern-Italian fizz with sweetish strawberry fruit (in spite of its 'extra dry' designation) and two principal merits: it's briskly interesting and fun, and it isn't prosecco; 11% alcohol.

🍷 7 Masottina Prosecco £10.00

Distinctly 'brut' style to this 'extra dry' Veneto foamer – a grown-up variation on the endlessly alluring Prosecco sweet fizzy-perry style; 11% alcohol.

🍷 8 Heretat El Padruell Cava Brut £8.50

Plenty of life in this lemony, fully sparkling Penedes wine; scores for vigour and freshness; 11.5% alcohol.

Morrisons

In the shake-up of supermarket retailing, Morrisons has emerged a winner. The Bradford-based chain has earned an enviably good name for customer service as well as competitive prices and, perhaps above all, for producing its own foods ('we're the second largest fresh food manufacturer in the UK') and sourcing from British farmers and processors. This looks a well-timed policy in the context of Brexit, the sagging of sterling and general alarm over our national food security.

I'm sure it all brings more customers into the wine department, and Morrisons continues to make improvements in the offering, even extending the range, while rivals – Tesco in particular – are reining back.

As with the other chains, Morrisons are focusing on their own-label wines. The basic 'Signature' range carries the name Wm Morrison as a script signature on the labels. The premium range, with commendable concision if not coyness, is called The Best. A lot of wines from both these selections feature in the following pages.

There is a new mini own-label range from Australia, called Workshop. It's been introduced, says wine manager Clive Donaldson, in response to customers who 'told us they wanted an alternative wine range to the big Australian brands'. Good for them. I particularly mention this, because Workshop McLaren Vale Shiraz 2015 at £12.00 is emphatically among my wines of the year.

Inevitably, you cannot expect to find every listed wine in every branch of Morrisons, but there is a dedicated website, Morrisons Cellar, from which you can order most of the range – and a number of online exclusives – for home delivery.

RED WINES

ARGENTINA

🍷 8 **The Best Malbec 2016** £7.00

Made for Morrisons by top outfit Catena, a muscular but not stringy Mendoza wine with blackberry relish and cushiony mouthfeel.

AUSTRALIA

🍷 10 **Workshop McLaren Vale Shiraz 2015** £12.00

The new Workshop range from Australia has been brought in as an alternative to the big Aussie brands. That's good news. This is dense in colour and texture with a whopping but discreet 15.5% alcohol, and generously loaded with lifting berry fruits; good-hearted wine entirely worth its price and the kind of modern oaked Shiraz I hope Australia will persist with.

🍷 9 **Workshop Single Vineyard Grenache Shiraz 2015** £12.00

This one, also from McLaren Vale, is light in colour but quite intensely plummy and sweet-spicy in its fruit with serious (again 15.5% alcohol) but controlled ripeness, elegant weight and seductive style; quite special, really.

CHILE

🍷 7 **Morrisons Carmenère 2015** £4.00

Very light (be warned if you like a bit of body) but toothsome juicy red berry party red that will chill happily.

🍷 8 **Head Honcho Merlot 2016** £6.50

Try not to let the scary anthropomorphic label deter you, because this sweetly ripe but healthily bouncy hedgerow-fruit picnic red is nicely balanced and wholesome.

🍷 8 **The Best Chilean Merlot 2015** £8.00

Trim, dark choc-and-cherry benchmark Colchagua Merlot, ripe and long and trimmed with a confident clean acidity; 13.5% alcohol.

RED WINES

Morrisons

CHILE

🍷 9 **Koyle Malbec 2011** £12.00
Chile lags behind its fractious neighbour Argentina in
the Malbec stakes but this contender from the Colchagua
Valley tips the odds. It's enticingly opaque, intensely
perfumed and ripe, benefiting from its long oak and bottle
ageing, optimising the Malbec's dark savour rather than
its macho toughness; a nicely wrought special occasion
wine; 14.5% alcohol.

🍷 9 **Errazuriz Max Reserva Carmenère 2014** £13.00
Deep crimson – or carmine – colour and a billow of ripe
berry fruits welcome you to this luxuriantly ripe and
savoury oaked roast-beef red from top Chilean producer
Errazuriz. Sweetly spiced with long, long flavours and
ideal balance, a special Carmenère indeed; 14% alcohol.

🍷 9 **Morrisons Claret 2015** £4.50
Jolly well put-together Merlot-led blend with convincing
colour, bright black-fruit juicy aromas and fruit all in
wholesome balance; an enticing bargain at this very low
price and better, I thought, than the pricier companion
Bordeaux 'Superior'.

FRANCE

🍷 10 **Beaujolais Alliance Des Vignerons 2016** £5.00
This is exactly as everyday Beaujolais should be: purple,
juicy, bouncing with new-squished fruit finishing clean
and brisk, refreshing the palate and the soul. At the price
a terrific bargain.

🍷 8 **The Best IGP Côtes Catalanes 2015** £7.50
Grenache/Carignan-led blend from the Languedoc with a
distinct garrigue character – that ineffable property of herb/
spice perfume from sun-baked wild hill country – to its
plentifully ripe dark fruits; 13.5% alcohol. Cassoulet red.

RED WINES

8 **The Best Red Burgundy 2015** £8.00
Gutsy generic Pinot Noir/Gamay blend; plenty of well-set raspberry-cherry fruit in good balance and plenty of tannin too; time might help.

8 **The Best Fleurie 2016** £8.25
Modestly priced for the most sought-after of the Beaujolais crus, this is a densely-coloured juicy wine of decent Beaujolais Villages character.

7 **Gerard Bertrand No Added Sulphite Cabernet 2016** £8.50
It's no mean feat to make healthy wine without sulphur products, so well done former French rugby captain M Bertrand for this offering to drinkers who cannot tolerate said products. You get inky mauve colour in this Languedoc wine and mildly scorched black fruits with a bitter-chocolate centre. Needs meaty-starchy food alongside.

8 **Gerard Bertrand Les Aspres Réserve 2014** £10.00
A surprise from the Languedoc fronted by a Rioja-like aroma of cassis enrobed in sweet vanilla. The gently spicy intense fruit stands up well to this oak-contact effect to make a fun velvety red of satisfying ripeness; 14% alcohol.

8 **Le Verdier Cairanne 2015** £10.00
Cairanne is a newly elevated appellation of the Côtes du Rhône, now enjoying the same status as Gigondas and Châteauneuf du Pape. Expect prices to rise accordingly, but meantime try this well-knit oak-fermented and raised spicy dark wine for its fine savour and grip; 13.5% alcohol.

FRANCE

RED WINES

Morrisons (vertical, left margin)

FRANCE

🍷 8　**The Best Lussac Saint-Emilion 2015**　　£10.00
Purple colour gives way to a pleasingly rounded sweet-cherry/cassis fruit with urbane claret mintiness and sleekness; an attractive package for now or for several years to come.

ITALY

🍷 8　**Villa Verde Montepulciano d'Abruzzo 2015** £4.50
The whiff of raisin to this purple-coloured and purple-tasting bright and juicy Adriatic red works nicely into the balance of sweetness and easy tannin; pizza partner at a keen price.

🍷 8　**Badia al Colle Chianti 2015**　　　£4.75
Cheap Chianti is in short supply and here's a drinkable one, healthily brambly and bright with easy weight and a crisp finish.

🍷 8　**Morrisons Montepulciano d'Abruzzo 2015** £6.00
A tauter, sleeker wine than the Villa Verde above, but still with bouncing juicy red fruit; for the more sophisticated, or less price-conscious, palate maybe.

🍷 8　**Morrisons Nero d'Avola 2016**　　　£6.00
Indigenous Sicilian wine from the black (nero) grape of the fine town of Avola, suitably dark in colour and plump with concentrated blackberry-savour fruit; welcome hint of caramel en route to a grippy finish.

🍷 8　**The Best Primitivo 2015**　　　　£6.75
Generous sweetly (but not too sweetly) ripe pure varietal from Puglia has enticing soft savour but finishes clean; 13.5% alcohol. Good barbecue red.

RED WINES

ITALY

9 **Contrade Bellusa Nerello Mascalese 2016** £7.50
Little-known grape Nerello Mascalese flourishes on the lower slopes of Sicily's grumbling giant Mount Etna. This one has a creamy character to its busy, brambly fruit, and makes a very pleasing contrast to the darker, denser Italian reds of the day; 13.5% alcohol.

8 **Nipozzano Chianti Riserva Vecchie Viti 2013** £24.00
An elegant and silkily oaked mature wine from the flagship estate of Florence's first family of wine, the Frescobaldis. It's from the lesser-known Chianti Rufina zone rather than the much-vaunted Chianti Classico, but one of the great names of the region nonetheless. Really quite good value at the price, but available only online.

NEW ZEALAND

9 **The Best Otago Pinot Noir 2015** £9.75
Taut style gives vigour and freshness to this lush ripe raspberry-strawberry oaked wine made by the well-regarded Mudhouse winery; slinky and long-flavoured; 14% alcohol.

8 **Pura Bay Pinot Noir 2015** £9.75
Plump soft summer red fruits abound in this mellow, earthy-minty trademark oaked Kiwi Pinot finishing bright and fresh; 14% alcohol.

S. AFRICA

8 **The Best South African Cabernet Sauvignon 2015** £7.00
Engaging pure varietal shows bright cassis ripeness rounded by oak contact and a leafy crispness at the top of the flavour; 14% alcohol.

Morrisons

RED WINES

S. AFRICA

🍷 8 **The Saviour Cinsault 2016** £7.00

One of several Cape Cinsaults I have much liked this year. Looks pale but the brambly fruit is firm and lingering, finishing brisk and clean; 14.5% alcohol.

SPAIN

🍷 8 **Morrisons Tempranillo 2016** £4.00

Straight healthy blackcurranty La Mancha wine at a great price.

🍷 8 **The Best Priorat 2014** £10.00

Truffle and cinnamon count among the pleasing evocations amid the toasty black fruit of this easy-weighted wine from the re-emerging Catalan DO of Priorat; 14.5% alcohol.

WHITE WINES

🍷 8 **Workshop Bench Blend Chardonnay 2016** £6.00

Yeoman unoaked modern peach/appley fresh varietal at a sensible price.

AUSTRALIA

🍷 8 **The Best Western Australia Chardonnay 2016** £8.00

Nostalgic note of sweet oaky lushness in this otherwise bracingly fresh mineral stone-fruit dry wine; 14% alcohol.

🍷 9 **The Best Grüner Veltliner 2015** £8.00

Very dry but not austere, this has an upfront citrus twang and lots of aromatic spicily abrading fruit; one of the best examples of this distinctive style I have tasted through the year.

CHILE

🍷 8 **Root 1 Sauvignon Blanc 2016** £8.00

Gimmicky bottling for an otherwise attractive asparagus and nettle aboundingly fresh Casablanca Valley wine with long flavours.

WHITE WINES

CHILE

8 Koyle Costa Sauvignon Blanc 2015 £13.00
This part oak-fermented luxury dry wine has a wild
asparagus whiff and flood of ripe even rich but grassily-
zesty flavours.

8 Les Richoises White 2016 £5.00
Meadow-flower freshness and bloom on the nose of this
tangy and agreeably grassy dry party wine from southwest
France; 11% alcohol.

8 Pomerols Picpoul de Pinet 2016 £6.50
The reasonable price is a draw but I liked this tangily
aromatic easy-drinking example of the popular
Mediterranean seafood partner on its own account.

8 The Best Muscadet de Sèvre et Maine
Sur Lie 2016 £7.00
Fresh but not green manifestation of the distinctive Loire
dry wine has briny tang and plenty of crisp white fruit;
nothing better matches moules.

FRANCE

8 The Best Touraine Sauvignon Blanc 2016 £7.50
Appropriately named as Touraine, now easily the best
source of generic Sauvignon; this one is crisp, tangy and
well-made with a nice lick of green ripeness.

8 Vinus Paul Mas Clairette 2016 £8.00
Hint of the exotic in this florally perfumed still dry white
from a grape variety much better known in its sparkling
manifestation at home in Pyrenean France; fresh and fun.

8 The Best Chablis 2015 £10.00
Mellow easy-drinking wine but well-defined for Chablis
style; appley, even brassica-like notes, with a white-nut
ripeness.

WHITE WINES

Morrisons

FRANCE

🍷 9 **The Best Pouilly-Fumé 2016**   £11.00
River-pebble-fresh zingy and lush pure Sauvignon from
suitably sited classic AC on the banks of the Loire;
thought-provoking grassy-nettly flavours, though no sign
of the smoke suggested in the name; keen price for this.

🍷 9 **The Best Chablis 1er Cru 2014**   £15.00
Immediately impressive gunflint and lime aromas from
a fine green-gold pure Chardonnay made in a legendary
Chablis vintage; this is showing very well and will evolve
but already long, minerally and lush.

ITALY

🍷 8 **The Best Verdicchio 2016**   £6.25
Crisp cabbage and lemon flavours (if that can be imagined)
are true to the style of this timeless Marches dry aperitif
white, complete with a lick of nutty sweetness.

🍷 8 **Sorso Pinot Grigio 2016**   £7.00
A much fuller, riper style of PG than expected, but this
one is from the Abruzzo, south of its home territory of
Veneto. Savoury, interesting dry wine with 14% alcohol.

🍷 8 **Masseria Pietrosa Verdeca 2015**   £8.00
Floral perfume welcomes you into this aromatic oak-
fermented Puglian dry wine, made from elusive local
Verdeca grape. Ripe, balanced and clearly a good food
match – fish and fowl.

MOLDOVA

🍷 9 **Morrisons Pinot Grigio 2016**   £4.25
A boldly brisk dry wine with a notion of smoky savour,
really quite good, and extremely cheap; Moldova is not
famous for its wines and deserves better.

WHITE WINES

NEW ZEALAND

9 **The Best New Zealand Sauvignon Blanc 2016** £8.00
Almost-startlingly brisk and steely, sherbet and gooseberry Marlborough wine by much-garlanded Yealands Estate, generous in lingering flavour and parsimonious in price.

8 **Leftfield Albariño 2016** £12.00
I'll say it's leftfield – Albariño is supposed to be made 12,000 miles away in Galicia, not in Gisborne. But here's a sort of super-extracted spin on the original with lashings of complex briny fruit, brash citrus twang and plenty of woof. At a price. Online only, I'm afraid.

S. AFRICA

8 **Morrisons Chardonnay 2017** £4.25
Attractive brassica-peach style to a brisk party dry white.

8 **Morrisons Chenin Blanc 2017** £4.25
Fruit-blossom nose with a trace of nectar leads into a delicately crisp freshness.

8 **The Best Rueda Canto Real Verdejo 2016** £6.00
Keen, green sea-breezy dry white to match to shellfish, especially oysters and mussels; good value.

8 **The Best Albariño 2016** £8.00
Big-flavoured Atlantic coast dry wine carries long grassy-briny flavours through to a fine lemony acidity.

SPAIN

9 **The Best Rioja Blanco Reserva 2013** £13.00
Splendid gold-coloured and vanilla-scented old-fashioned oaked Rioja in the brilliantly gaudy livery of Bodega Marques de Los Rios. A real find for questers of the fast-disappearing oxidative style, although in fairness it's really quite fresh and bright in the modern way.

SPARKLING WINES

8 The Best Champagne Rosé £20.00
Perky salmon colour, strawberry-tart nose and matching
friendly fruit, fresh not sweet at all, dry but not austere;
a safe pink champagne that tastes like pink champagne.

7 Menestrello Spumante Bianco £8.00
It's from Garganega, the grape that makes briskly dry
Soave in Verona, but it tastes like Moscato as in Asti
Spumante; not too sweet, though, and decent balance
too; 11% alcohol. Try instead of prosecco (try anything
instead of prosecco).

8 The Best Prosecco £8.50
It says 'crisp and fresh' on the label and pretty much
lives up to it – lively elderflower style, crispish pear fruit,
dryish style; 11% alcohol.

7 Valbello Prosecco Asolo £10.00
The designation is 'extra-dry' but it isn't; sweetness is all-
too evident in the peary foam, but it's quite a fun (though
pricey) frother for all that.

9 The Best Vintage Cava Brut 2014 £7.00
Cava, the proper Catalan fizz knocked off its perch by
presumptuous prosecco, may have lost out through its
relative harshness of style. This has a certain mellow
breadiness I liked, and has lots of appley verve, finishing
brisk and fresh. Good and very good value.

Sainsbury's

Have you heard the old joke? It's attributed to humorist Alan Coren, late father of famous siblings Giles and Victoria. 'Sainsbury's,' he declared, 'was invented to keep the riff-raff out of Waitrose.'

Nonsense of course. Sainsbury's was invented in 1869, a generation before Messrs Waite and Rose (along with somebody called Taylor) first opened up shop in 1904. But Coren was a shrewd observer of human folly and its especial manifestation in the British class system, and his outrageous gag still rings true.

But who doesn't love Sainsbury's? Wine lovers certainly should. Back in the 1980s Sainsbury's led the way in supermarket wine. They brought in the first own-label ranges. And they have continued to lead the way in wine right now.

It's the Taste the Difference range that sets the standard. Half the wines I have picked out this year are TTD, and include two top scores, perennial favourite dry white Greco di Tufo 2016 from Italy's Campania at £9.00 and a new wine, Côtes du Rhône Blanc 2015, at £7.00.

One section of the TTD range that I have not reviewed this year is the sherry collection. I have not retasted them since last year's edition but am willing to vouch for their perpetual merit. Look out particularly for the piercingly pungent and tangy Fino and the toasty-figgy, piquant and perfectly dry 12-Year-Old Amontillado, both at a bargain £8.00.

Sainsbury's is persisting with regular promotions on its wines, offering 25 per cent off the whole range for limited periods several times a year – almost invariably coinciding with similar Tesco campaigns, I notice. As there are always individual wines on promo, this can give rise to discounts near to 50 per cent.

RED WINES

ARGENTINA

9 DV Catena Malbec 2014 £12.00
An iron-hand-in-velvet-glove Malbec from some very
high-altitude vineyards (up to 1,450 metres) in the Andean
province of Mendoza. There is a deliciously roasty core to
the black-fruit flavours of this oak-rich food red (grand
barbecue maybe?) and it tastes reassuringly expensive;
14% alcohol.

**9 Taste the Difference Château Tanunda
Barossa Cabernet Merlot 2015** £10.00
Opaque crimson colour and blooming cassis nose
define this extraordinary Bordeaux-style Barossa from
Australia's oldest 'chateau' (est 1890). It's silky and
cedary and finely poised, wearing its 15% alcohol lightly.

AUSTRALIA

**9 Barossa Valley Estate Grenache
Shiraz Mourvèdre 2015** £12.00
The supple, juicy, rounded and comforting black-fruit
flavours in this sunnily ripe monster come in a layered yet
entirely cohesive wave; a muscular but elegant modern
Aussie wine that is unquestonably, if ineffably, special;
14% alcohol.

FRANCE

9 Domaine du Colombier Chinon 2014 £7.00
Ripe, vigorous and leafy-fresh bold redcurrant Cabernet
Franc from the Loire is on fine form in this vintage.
Serve gently chilled to boost the refreshment factor in
this distinctive wine. And ignore the back-label advice
to drink within two years – Chinon reds can age very
gracefully indeed.

RED WINES

9 Taste the Difference Languedoc Rouge 2015 £7.00

I'm expecting – hoping for – a successful 2016 vintage of this dark, spicy and savoury Mediterranean perennial but did not get a taste before deadline. If you find the 2015 (praised to the skies here in last year's edition), don't hesitate, but keep a look out for the new vintage too; 13.5% alcohol.

8 Duc de Castellac Bergerac Rouge 2015 £7.00

Bergerac is Bordeaux's much-less-vaunted neighbour, making red wines from the same grape varieties that rarely benefit from comparison. Here's a good one: vigorous blackcurrant fruit with sunny mellowness and a nice tannic clench.

9 Taste the Difference Pic St Loup 2015 £8.00

Welcome return to form for this hardy Languedoc perennial, coming over big and spicy with a fine dark sleekness in the excellent harvest year of 2015. It's an unoaked wine and given its natural ripeness a modest 12.5% alcohol. Enjoy it while the price is modest too, as Pic St Loup's imminent AOC status could prompt a hike.

9 Sancerre Rouge Les Champs Clos 2015 £13.00

I am often mystified by the appeal of Sancerre's expensive red wines, but this is a Pinot Noir with a clear purpose and identity, pure in varietal style, silky in the mouth and ideally weighted and balanced; hard to explain, easy to enjoy and worth the investment.

RED WINES

GERMANY

🍷 9 **Taste the Difference Rheinhessen Pinot Noir 2016**   £7.00

Niersteiner red burgundy, you might call it, this has proper pale but glowing Pinot colour, clean even crunchy raspberry-cherry fruit with a pomegranate note and a light but lush deliciousness that diverts the attention; fine warm-weather red to drink cool with delicate menus.

ITALY

🍷 8 **Taste the Difference Chianti Classico 2014** £9.00

Already showing orange at the edge of the colour and a suggestion of the spirit of old Chianti, this early developer has a gaminess to its briary juiciness, some oak contact and a satisfying weight; 13.5% alcohol.

🍷 9 **Taste the Difference Barbaresco 2013**   £11.00

Up in price but oft-discounted, this vintage has now been on shelf more than a year and is improving materially with age. The limpid ruby colour is browning at the edge and the delicate tea-and-roses aroma is blooming nicely; red-berry fruit is slinky and luxuriously complex with 13.5% alcohol; a fine introduction to one of Italy's great wine styles.

🍷 9 **Taste the Difference Valpolicella Ripasso 2014**   £11.00

Made by macerating Valpolicella in the vats in which Amarone has just been made and racked off the skins, the ripasso style is becoming wildly popular. This one is a case in point, dark intense and wholesomely raisiny, it's juicy and bright besides, taking on smoothness and nuance from 14 months ageing in oak; 14% alcohol.

Sainsbury's

RED WINES

ITALY

🍷 8 **Taste the Difference Amarone 2012** £16.00
Inspiration for the Ripasso wine immediately preceding this, Amarone is made from grapes dried out to two-thirds of their new-picked weight so the juice is concentrated to raisin-like sweetness. The long, slow fermentation produces wine of deep colour and intensity, dark and spicy plushness and a 'bitter' (amarone) dryness. This relatively inexpensive example meets all these criteria; 14.5% alcohol.

PORTUGAL

🍷 9 **Taste the Difference Douro 2015** £9.00
Agreeable porty fieriness in the spicy dark nose of this fine port-country table wine by Quinta do Crasto. The black fruit is sleek and deliciously spiky with minty-plummy savours but it is by no means overweight; 14% alcohol.

SPAIN

🍷 8 **Taste the Difference Viñedos
Barrihuelo Rioja Crianza 2014** £7.00
From busy Bodegas Muriel, a softly ripe, sweet-toffee-oaked pure Tempranillo with good blackcurranty piquancy; contrives to be intriguing; 13.5% alcohol.

🍷 9 **Ribera del Duero Condado de Haza 2012** £15.00
Creamily-oaked bumper pure Tempranillo with all the silky-minty, intense black fruit you're entitled to expect from the haughty heights of the Ribera, Spain's loftiest and most chi-chi vineyard region. From the Fine Wine range, it's often helpfully discounted; 13.5% alcohol.

RED WINES

USA

 8 **Taste the Difference Zinfandel Paso Robles 2015** £10.00

Raisiny recognisable Zinfandel (same grape as Puglia's Primitivo) from California's highlands carrying soft blackberry ripeness with a lick of marzipan to a clean grippy flavour edge to satisfy the senses; 14.5% alcohol.

PINK WINES

FRANCE

8 **Taste the Difference Fronton Négrette Rosé 2016** £7.00

Inoffensive salmon pink colour, easy soft summer red fruits in a very dry, almost austere, style, from the Toulouse region; versatile food matcher.

8 **Baron Gassier Sainte Victoire Elégance Côtes de Provence Rosé 2016** £12.00

Discreetly coloured dry wine offering fresh strawberry and redcurrant fruits in fine balance; proper rosé that tastes, well, pink. A pricey item but there's a kind of saving in the magnum-size bottle at £20.00.

8 **Miraval Rosé 2016** £18.00

Fine new vintage for this expensive Provencal pink in what was not such a good year for celebrity owners Brad Pitt and Angelina Jolie. Enticing coral colour, summer-floral and strawberry perfume, delicate corresponding fruit, fresh and assured.

Sainsbury's

WHITE WINES

🍷 **9** **Taste the Difference Chateau Tanunda Australian Chardonnay 2016** £7.00
Friendly part-oaked bargain with ripe stone-fruit lushness and a palpable minerality; lively, balanced and 13.5% alcohol. The score reflects my experience of buying this at just £4.50 in a promotion – a real steal.

🍷 **8** **McGuigan Shortlist Riesling 2016** £14.00
Premium wine from the Hunter Valley giant is a fine gold colour, granny-smith perfumed and generous with its racy fruit; big, confidently made Riesling to match fish dishes, white meats, poultry and more.

🍷 **8** **Taste the Difference Austrian Riesling 2016** £8.00
Elegant aperitif from the banks of the Danube; brisk and racy with an affecting balance of honeyed crisp-apple fruit and citrus edginess.

🍷 **8** **Taste the Difference Grüner Veltliner 2016** £8.00
Fresh and lively but full-bodied and exotic dry agreeable spicy aperitif wine which also makes a match for highly seasoned menus; scores for heft and nuance.

🍷 **8** **Valdivieso Reserva Sauvignon Blanc 2016** £8.00
Creamy yet cleverly crisp Casablanca dry wine showing clear grassy Sauvignon character with an underlying sweet mint, very much the Chilean style.

🍷 **7** **Changyu Noble Dragon Riesling 2013** £9.00
The shape of things to come? I can only assume Sainsbury wishes to sponsor Sino-European trade relations by importing this unnecessary token, but it's perfectly decent wine made in the Aussie style, dry and sinewy with a trace of lime by visiting Austrian winemaker Lenz Moser. Drink with Szechuan dishes, I imagine.

AUSTRALIA · *AUSTRIA* · *CHILE* · *CHINA*

WHITE WINES

ENGLAND

♈ 7 Chapel Down Flint Dry 2015 £10.00

A blend mainly of Chardonnay and Pinot Blanc harvested across Essex, Kent and Sussex, this has a delicate country-wine elderflower aroma and a fresh, dry style all its own with 11.5% alcohol. At this price, a wine for patriots.

♈ 10 Taste the Difference Côtes du Rhône White 2015 £7.00

A new wine at Sainsbury's, and to me, a revelation. Made from the sort of grape blend that goes into fabulously expensive white Châteaneuf du Pape, it delivers a basket of flavours encompassing peaches and apricots, soft pear and traces of honey, vanilla and sweet spice; all this in a medium of lush plumpness balanced by citrus twang; an exciting wine with versatile food-matching properties, and a bargain.

FRANCE

♈ 8 Taste the Difference Bordeaux Sauvignon Blanc 2016 £7.00

Elegant, delicate, even genteel are words that come to mind. Dry white Bordeaux has always been Sauvignon based but quite distinct from its stony-steely counterparts in the Loire. This one is spare, pure and tight, but not spartan or tart. A refined very dry Sauvignon of distinctive style.

♈ 8 Taste the Difference Muscadet 2016 £7.00

Lemony-leesy Muscadet of a very correct kind, and not too fierce in its acidity; the definitive partner to mussels.

WHITE WINES

🍷 8 Vouvray La Couronne des Plantagenets 2016 £7.00

This long-standing Sainsbury's favourite is a lusciously ripe pure Chenin Blanc from a famed appellation of the Loire; seductive honeysuckle-scented white fruits with nifty limey twang to balance; this is a plush dry aperitif of unique style.

🍷 9 Taste the Difference Touraine Sauvignon Blanc 2016 £7.50

The generic 'Touraine' (province of the city of Tours) in the Loire Valley is a designation to seek out these days in the worldwide quest for good Sauvignon Blanc. This one is a typical thriller: nettly nose, rush of grassy-lush fruit, crisp, breezy and stimulating; surpasses just about anything from New Zealand at this price.

🍷 8 La Grande Nuit Chardonnay 2016 £7.50

Languedoc wine seems to have been made in the Mâconnais style, sleek and mineral and with a portion matured in oak; pleasing peachy ripeness.

🍷 9 Signé Montagny 2014 £9.50

Decent white burgundy at under a tenner is an endangered species, so seek out this lovely Chalonnais. You get generous colour, luscious stone fruit flavours, bright minerality – the whole caboodle – and made without recourse to oak. An artful contrivance indeed.

🍷 8 Chablis Premier Cru Brocard 2014 £18.00

Steely but lavish top-flight Chablis from famed Domaines Brocard has classic green-gold colour, forceful Chardonnay perfume and leesy richness; no oak here but it's Chablis all the way – at a price.

WHITE WINES

GERMANY

🍷 8 **Taste the Difference German Pinot
Blanc 2016**   £7.00

Interesting diversion from the Mosel, a racier kind of
Pinot Blanc than the genteel Alsace style. It has the grape's
signature appley-leafy aromas and fine freshness. Pinot
Blanc is much better known in Germany, incidentally, as
Weissburgunder.

🍷 8 **Taste the Difference Pinot Grigio
Trentino 2016**   £7.00

Above bog-standard PG owes its extra interest to the
15% Chardonnay in the blend; fresh, aromatic and crisp.

🍷 10 **Taste the Difference Greco di Tufo 2016**   £9.00

I believe this is the best vintage ever of this handsomely
presented hardy perennial. Greco's the name of the grape,
first planted in the Campania by Greeks millennia ago,
and Tufo is the regional soil formed from the region's
volcanic rock. The wine has a gold colour and aromas that
evoke the sun-seared, spicily scented landscape, evoking
fruits from apricot and apple to melon and peach, and
herbal notes of fennel and sage. It's exotic and complex,
but bright and fresh besides. Great match for creamy
pasta, grilled fish, chicken dishes and pongy cheese.

🍷 8 **Taste the Difference Vermentino 2016**   £9.00

From the Salento peninsula rather than indigenous
Sardinia, this rather grand Vermentino hits the spot: fresh
and tangy with grapefruit lift and a nice lick of white-nut
richness alongside.

ITALY

WHITE WINES

8 Mount Rozier The Flower Garden Sauvignon Blanc 2016 £8.50

More seagrass than flowers, I'd say, but it's tangy and fresh without being too challenging; 13.5% alcohol.

8 Brancott Terroir Series Sauvignon Blanc 2016 £10.00

Brancott, behemoth of the New Zealand wine industry, is branching out into regional wines. This Awatere, Marlborough, Sauvignon has customary asparagus and gooseberry notes but in an untypically rich and leesy medium which certainly grabs the attention; keen balance, though, and a departure from the formulaic.

8 Stellenrust Stellenbosch Manor Chenin Blanc 2016 £8.00

Particularly brisk and bright-tasting Chenin which still manages to reveal a seductive honeysuckle richness en route to a very dry, lemon-tinged finish; 13.5% alcohol.

10 Stellenrust Stellenbosch Manor Barrel-Fermented Chenin Blanc 2016 £13.00

The Corton-Charlemagne of the Cape? The weight and intensity of this lavishly oaked dry white does suggest Burgundian Chardonnay, but the Cape's Chenin Blanc reveals itself by way of the honeysuckle keynote deep in the basket of orchard and exotic fruits. There's a brilliant balancing citrus acidity to complete the exciting, uplifting effect and 13.5% alcohol. Shellfish matcher and a friend to poultry too.

NEW ZEALAND

SOUTH AFRICA

WHITE WINES

Y 9 **Taste the Difference Albariño 2016**   £8.00
Sainsbury's pioneered this Galician wine a decade ago
among the first of the new Taste the Difference range,
and it has been consistently brilliant. This new vintage is
bristling with briny vigour and lush with broad, green-
fruit flavours; a big, ripe and satisfying dry wine to
complement every kind of seafood; 13.5% alcohol.

Y 8 **Colinas de Uruguay Albariño 2016**   £8.00
A tangy, briny and sunnily ripe spin on Spain's Rias
Baixas model, from vineyards, like those of Galicia
thousands of miles to the northeast, close to the Atlantic
shore, buffeted by ocean winds and constant rain. I liked
this: Viva Uruguay!

SPARKLING WINES

Y 8 **Taste the Difference Crémant de Loire**   £11.00
Busily fizzy Chenin Blanc-Chardonnay blend from Saumur
with honey-lemon enticements all in the 'Brut' dry style.

Y 10 **Winemakers' Selection Champagne**
          Blanc de Noirs Brut   £20.00
The record's getting stuck here. This is my favourite
supermarket NV champagne (closely rivalled by the Co-
op's current Les Pionniers, I'll admit) year after year. You
get an enticing bready aroma, long, focused fruit flavours
carried along by the flowing mousse and a genuinely
uplifting freshness and balance.

Y 8 **Winemakers' Selection Champagne**
          Blanc de Blancs Brut   £20.00
All-Chardonnay non-vintage but mature-tasting sparkler
has a fine soft mellowness and makes extremely easy
drinking.

SPAIN

URUGUAY

FRANCE

Tesco

Tesco is back. It's been a bad patch for the Juggernaut, but 2017 has brought a return to profitable trading. That's what matters. Regaining the esteem, even affection, once felt by the shopping public might take a little longer.

The wine range has been severely pruned during Tesco's lengthy downturn. Many favourite items, including numerous own-labels, have been excised. This year to my relief there have been some new additions to the 'Finest' range, and some of these make honourable appearances in the following pages.

I have not been able to try as many of their wines as I would like during 2017 because, yet again, Tesco has not staged a tasting for the press in time for summer–autumn deadlines. I cannot understand, when all the other major retailers who feature in this guide put on tastings, why Tesco – by far the biggest of them all – refuses to do so.

Searching for a recipe in a favourite cookbook, Nigel Slater's *Kitchen Diaries* the other day, I came across this aside from the author: 'I have honestly never set foot inside a branch of Tesco'. As an advocate of supermarkets, I did rather recoil at the loftiness of this remark. But it's a free country. We can all pick and choose.

RED WINES

ARGENTINA

🍷 9   **Finest The Trilogy Malbec 2015**   £11.00
Unexpectedly pale violet colour and a sweet pomegranate-juice aroma immediately intrigue the senses. This is not your tough, chewy kind of high-country Andean Malbec, but your cushiony, wildly ripe and smoothly satisfying kind. Drink now with rare beef or keep for years and expect developments. Made by ace producer Catena from the harvests of three well-rated vineyards, all at 'exceptionally high altitude' in the Mendoza region; 13.5% alcohol.

CHILE

🍷 8   **Terrunyo Carmenère 2015**   £18.00
Lavish, but ideally weighted prestige brand of giant Concha y Toro is silky, spicy and abrim with black fruits; a Chilean spin on the style of classed-growth claret: equally interesting at a fraction of the price; 14.5% alcohol.

FRANCE

🍷 8   **Tesco Côtes du Rhône 2015**   £4.00
Simple, respectable and ripe middleweight of typical character is very cheap; 13.5% alcohol.

🍷 8   **Beaujolais 2016**   £4.50
Soft and light-bodied' proclaims the front label of this reliable perennial, purple-bright in this vintage and crunchily fruity in the proper manner; at its best served straight from the fridge.

🍷 7   **Finest St Chinian 2015**   £7.00
It's £2 cheaper than the launch 2013 vintage and, I believe, lighter in weight, stronger in intensity and interest, too; gently spicy easy-drinking Languedoc food red with 13.5% alcohol.

RED WINES

Tesco

FRANCE

🍷 **10** **Finest Faugères 2015** £8.00

Impressive package among the new additions to the Finest range; immediately likeable, dark in fruit and savour with blackberry bite and spicy-herby aromas. Faugères can get overheated and tough, but this one is notably friendly and firm. The back label advice is 'To enjoy this wine at its best, drink within five years of purchase'. No doubt true, but it's certainly ready to enjoy now, with meat, game or starchy cassoulet. Top buy.

🍷 **9** **Finest Médoc 2015** £8.00

Elegant, minty, perfectly weighted proper claret already mellow for drinking now and repays decanting; attractive package from reliable negociant Yvon Mau. Ignore back-label advice to drink within two years – this should do very nicely in the longer term.

🍷 **8** **Finest Minervois La Livinière 2015** £9.50

Nice presentation among the 2017 additions to the Finest range, a dark and warmly spicy food red (cassoulet will do nicely) with a comfortingly roasted note to the black fruit and, to borrow from Tesco's own note about it, flavours reminiscent of tapenade; 13.5% alcohol.

ITALY

🍷 **8** **Finest Montepulciano d'Abruzzo 2015** £6.00

Bouncy-juicy-brambly spaghetti wine of wholesome charm with generous weight and a convincingly clean finish.

🍷 **8** **Finest Lambrusco Reggiano Rosso Amabile** £7.00

In the context of Tesco's radical cutdown on the diversity of its range, this new addition to the list suggests redemptive capriciousness. It's great, and good value – an authentic dry (but not raspingly dry) and joyously fruity perkily fizzy example of the Emilia-Romagna classic to serve very cold on picnics; the original Lambrusco, at just 8% alcohol.

RED WINES

7 Finest Barbera d'Alba 2014   £8.00
Made by Piedmont giant Fratelli Martini, a long-term
Tesco supplier and rather good at plumply oaked Barbera,
I was expecting this to be a big, bouncy blueberry fruit
bomb, but it turns out rather lean. Restrained, I suppose,
and respectable; 14% alcohol

10 Lava Beneventano Aglianico 2012   £8.50
Another spiffing vintage for this deluxe Campania red-
meat varietal, smoothly dark and spicy with what might
be an imagined scorch of brimstone where the fruit meets
the clean, dry edge of the flavour. The Aglianico grape,
once known as Ellenico after the Greeks who first planted
the variety in this volcanic region 2,500 years ago, has a
distinct ancient gravitas all its own, accentuated by the
extravagantly heavy retro bottle it comes in.

8 Ca'Marrone Rosso Puglia
Appassimento 2015   £8.50
Odd-looking bottle with gaudy livery reveals a big, bold,
sweet-cherry meat and strong-cheese matcher made with
the addition of must from sun-dried Merlot grapes; it's
a variation on the Veronese amarone theme and pretty
rustic, but macho thirsts may well warm to it; 14.5%
alcohol and frequently discounted.

8 Finest Valpolicella Ripasso Cantina
Valpantena 2014   £11.00
An old Tesco favourite in new livery (and at an elevated
price) this is as satisfyingly dark and weighty as ever, the
cherry fruit plumped up through steeping on the grape
skins to fashion a fine balance between bright fruit and
rich savour; fab match for roasts or exotic baked pasta;
13.5% alcohol.

ITALY

RED WINES

N. ZEALAND

🍷 **9** **Finest Marlborough Pinot Noir 2015**   £8.00
Attractive jewel-like ruby colour and sweetly ripe cherry pong carry you into this delightful confection of soft, cushiony black-cherry-strawberry fruit all in successful balance; distinctive wine in its weight as well as its fruit, and enhanced by discreet chilling.

SPAIN

🍷 **9** **Finest Viña del Cura Rioja Reserva 2012**   £8.00
Reassuringly vanilla-creamy new vintage for Tesco perennial mysteriously renamed last year from 'Mara' to present 'Cura' is emphatic in its sweet-cassis depth and skin-on plummy grippiness; modern, muscular Rioja with maturing potential.

🍷 **8** **Finest Ribera del Duero Reserva 2012**   £8.00
Solid new vintage not quite as overwhelming as the 2011 is nevertheless impressively dense, with cassis fruit, creamy from oak contact and full of interest; 14% alcohol.

🍷 **9** **Finest Viña del Cura Rioja Gran
Reserva 2010**   £10.00
Luxuriantly good, with wild berry fruit aromas and laced with intense blackcurrant fruit given luxury richness by long contact with new(ish) American oak; in nice balance – the vanilla doesn't overwhelm the juiciness – you get what you pay for; 13.5% alcohol.

🍷 **8** **Viña Mayor Ribera del Duero
Reserva 2011**   £16.00
Proper chewy all-Tempranillo heavyweight from prestigious region, fancifully priced but frequently discounted by as much as half. Sleek, blackcurranty oaked style ageing nicely; 14% alcohol.

WHITE WINES

AUSTRALIA

Y 8 **Finest Tingleup Riesling 2016**   £8.00
Intriguing whiff of grapefruit from this limey Great
Southern dry varietal leads on to lots of crunchy red-apple
fruit and lemon twang with a softish edge suggesting a
lick of residual sugar. Easy-going aperitif so-named by
its maker for the way it tingles up the tastebuds of the
appreciative drinker. Well, maybe.

FRANCE

Y 8 **Finest Côtes de Gascogne Colombard
Gros Manseng 2016**   £6.00
This is a rebranding in the Finest range of the old Tesco
Côtes de Gascogne Blanc, nicely made by Gascon co-op
Producteurs Plaimont to deliver a seaside (Atlantic) fresh
dry wine with tang and citrus over an artfully peachy
undercurrent of sunny flavour; 11% alcohol. Note this
replaces the Finest Côtes de Gascogne Gros Manseng
Sauvignon Blanc of happy memory under the same livery,
now deleted from the list.

Y 7 **Tesco Côtes de Thau 2016**   £6.00
Sauvignon Blanc leads the flavour in this fresh blend
with Terret grapes from vineyards neighbouring better-
known Mediterranean appellation of Picpoul de Pinet.
The curiousness of the tapered bottle is matched by the
quirkiness of the style, reminding one taster of artichoke.

Y 8 **Tesco Muscadet de Sèvre et Maine Sur
Lie 2016**   £6.50
Briny-nosed and tangy, in the customary style of this
Loire-estuary mussel-matcher, there is less of the green
acidity that can make these wines a bit too challenging;
nice commercial example.

WHITE WINES

FRANCE

7 Finest Gaillac Perlé 2016   £7.00
Dry-ish aperitif wine from 'rare local grapes' showed
none of the 'delicate bubbles' claimed on the back label,
but it did deliver some of the fresh citrus and stone fruit
(pear, more like) also advertised. All in all, an enjoyable
summer refresher from an unfashionable region (Gaillac)
in a very attractive bottle.

9 Finest Viré Clessé 2015   £11.00
Love this elegant, minerally burgundy in the authentic
regional style, bright and tangy, oaked in parts with
the trademark saucy sweet mintiness of the best of the
Mâconnais.

GERMANY

8 Finest Steillage Mosel Riesling 2015   £6.00
Pale, delicate and just-detectably spritzy aperitif wine
of discreet charm, off-dry in style, fresh and brisk with
proper Riesling red-apple juiciness.

ITALY

8 Tesco Fiano 2016   £5.00
Bold, crisp first taste to this Cantine Settesoli-made
Sicilian perennial. You get lots of apple and pear fruit
with a nice Sicilian-citrus twang at the edge. Good match
for oily fish; 13.5% alcohol.

NEW ZEALAND

8 Wairau Cove Sauvignon Blanc 2016   £6.50
Infallible Marlborough annual, endearingly easy drinking,
crisp and grassy with clear gooseberry notes and a lick of
tropical lushness; good value; 11.5% alcohol.

7 Finest Marlborough Sauvignon Blanc 2016 £7.00
Floral aroma and soft flowery fruit style are more to the
fore than expected grassiness and twang; genteel wine for
the cautious palate, I'd say.

WHITE WINES

NEW ZEALAND

9 **Finest North Road Vineyard Sauvignon Blanc 2016** £13.00
Nicely focused minerally Marlborough wine with arresting flavours of green fruits and citrus tang; made by famed Villa Maria estate and, I notice, two quid cheaper than when introduced a couple of years ago; 13.5% alcohol.

S. AFRICA

8 **Finest Breede River Sauvignon Blanc 2016** £6.00
Brightly nettly Stellenbosch wine showing great Sauvignon character with highlights of asparagus and lush green grass on the nose and palate – good value.

FORTIFIED WINES

PORTUGAL

9 **Finest 10-Year-Old Tawny Port** £12.00
More ruby than tawny in colour, but this consistent wood-aged wine has very proper tawny characteristics: creamy, nutty-figgy and minty with a nice ardent spiritousness alongside the sweet lushness of the fruit; in Portugal they drink this style of port chilled as an aperitif – very wise; 20% alcohol.

SPAIN

9 **Finest Amontillado Sherry 50cl** £6.00
Beautiful bronze colour, perfume of roasted fruits, eager nutty-figgy flavours edged with citrus tang and dark savours, a wonderful naturally dry sherry by top bodega Barbadillo to drink well chilled in a decent-sized glass with nuts, olives or bold cheeses like manchego; 18.5% alcohol.

SPARKLING WINES

ENGLAND

🍷 8 **Finest English Sparkling Brut** £17.50
From a 500-year-old Kentish farm which first ventured
into vine-growing just 15 years ago. This lively fizz,
from the same grape varieties that go into champagne,
is convincingly apple-fresh with the right bready savour
and firm but not fierce acidity; the price seems unusually
reasonable for domestic fizz; 11.5% alcohol.

FRANCE

🍷 8 **Finest 1531 Blanquette de Limoux 2015** £9.00
Eager as I always am to suggest sparkling alternatives
to prosecco, here's a bangingly good frother from
deepest southwest France, bearing the commemorative
date of its first manufacture by the monks of Limoux.
That's a century before Dom Perignon was born and
an aeon earlier than the sorcerers of prosecco went into
production. This is brut dry but generously fruity and
fulfilling – and two quid cheaper than the last vintage I
tried, the 2012.

🍷 9 **Finest Premier Cru Champagne Brut** £19.00
It is axiomatic in the champagne business that non-vintage
brands should have a consistent style; true aficionados
can recognise a Bollinger, a Lanson or a Pol Roger at
first sniff. This Tesco perennial is in the same league –
boulangerie nose, fine tiny-bubble mousse, a mellowness
of Chardonnay-dominated fruit in ideal harmony with
freshness and vivid liveliness; top buy.

Waitrose

'We are really proud of our investment in quality at all levels,' says Waitrose wine boss Pierpaolo Petrassi MW, 'from our £4.99 range all the way to sending Xenia and Daphne to Bordeaux to buy for this year's En Primeur range.'

This seems to sum up the Waitrose wine experience very nicely. They really do offer lots of good wines in the 'entry level' price range. And of course Waitrose excels in the upper echelons with similar distinction. Claret, from the selections made at the châteaux by Xenia Irwin MW and Daphne Teremetz to the humblest 'Waitrose Good Ordinary' (10 out of 10 for the current superb 2015 vintage, price £5.19) is a particular strength in a list extending to something like a thousand different wines.

While Waitrose is very good about bringing in wines from unexpected places – Macedonia, Moldova and Slovenia all get a look-in – the classic regions are the real source of interest. The Sancerre from Alphonse Mellot is my favourite from the Loire this year, and the St Aubin from Gérard Thomas is just the sort of Beaune I like to pick, on my just-about-managing burgundy budget.

You get to taste wonderful champagnes at Waitrose. I am glad to report that the recently released 2009 vintage Louis Roederer Cristal (fruitcake on the nose, I have rashly averred) is a high scorer in spite of the price (£160.00). But I have given top score to Waitrose's own Special Reserve Vintage 2005 Champagne Brut at £24.99. Buttered-toast aroma this time, be warned.

Waitrose is not above energetic price promotions on its wines. There are monthly-changing offers on large numbers of individual wines, reducing prices by as much as a third. And there are occasional blanket promotions too. Worth keeping an eye out.

Online, Waitrose Cellar offers the whole range plus many online exclusives. You can buy by the individual bottle and any discounts current in store apply equally.

RED WINES

ARGENTINA

8 Colomé Malbec 2014 £17.49
Biodynamic vineyards up to an unfeasible-sounding 2,600 metres above sea level in the Salta Valley of the Andes provide the thick-skinned super-ripened fruit for this bible-black friendly monster with sweetly ripe toasty-roasty spicy black flavours neatly balanced by taut acidity; 'iconic' wine (to quote Waitrose) showing off Argentina at its best; 14.5% alcohol.

AUSTRALIA

8 Kilikanoon Grenache/Shiraz/ Mourvèdre 2016 £10.99
Plums and spice figure in the depths of this well-knit blend on the Rhône model with the additional ripeness and intensity you're entitled to expect from Down Under; 14.5% alcohol but not without poised balance.

9 Penfolds Max's Shiraz 2015 £18.99
Penfolds, once a ubiquitous Aussie brand here in Blighty, has lately seemed notably absent, but here's a fine tribute to the firm's legendary winemaker Max Schubert, creator of Grange Hermitage. Described on the back label as 'medium-bodied' this Shiraz has deep purple colour, big briary nose and layered fruits taking in blackberry and red berry fruits, smoothly flowing and, in rightful homage to the late Max's trademark, perfect balance; 14.5% alcohol.

BULGARIA

8 Zagreus St Dimitar Shiraz 2016 £6.99
From the once-familiar plain of Plovdiv, a remember-me wine of healthy blackberry charm, ripe and balanced; 13.5% alcohol.

RED WINES

CHILE

🍷 **9** **De Martino Old Vine Cinsault 2016** £10.99
Pale-looking and easy in weight, firmly focused red berry
fruits define this deliciously distinctive red from the Itata
Valley, birthplace 500 years ago of Chilean viticulture.
A hugely attractive wine that needs to be tried – should
match all kinds of menu – to be understood.

🍷 **9** **Cuvée Chasseur 2016** £4.99
A Waitrose stalwart: a humble Vin de France from
Narbonne but substantially coloured – nice crimson
– and ripe with wholesomely brambly and warmingly
spiced fruits in happy balance; a very dependable bargain.

🍷 **10** **Waitrose Good Ordinary Claret 2015** £5.19
This is more than good, it's great. Dark, integrated
Merlot-dominated generic Bordeaux of healthy, forward
blackcurrant fruitiness nicely rounded, supple and
balanced. Made by giant Bordeaux outfit Calvet but a
claret with real personality from a fine (though mixed)
vintage and at a giveaway price.

FRANCE

🍷 **8** **Remy Ferbras Ventoux 2016** £7.79
Ventoux, the famed mountain appellation of the southern
Rhône, is a watchword for inspiring wine. This one is
piquant on the nose and lipsmacking to the taste, intense
and savoury; 14% alcohol.

🍷 **8** **Esprit des Trois Pierres Costières de
Nîmes 2016** £7.99
A rush of ripe violet-tinged blackberry fruit sets up this
typical Costières de Nîmes nicely; easy-weighted wine in
its own style.

RED WINES

 8 Fitou Cuvée Madame Claude
Parmentier 2015 £7.99
Revival of the distinctive brand that made famous the
first (1946) AOC of the Languedoc back in the 1970s.
This is true to its yeoman origins, dark and sinewy, juicy
and vigorous with the ripe spiciness evoking the garrigue
landscapes of the sun-baked south.

8 Malbec de Balthazar Pays d'Oc 2016 £7.99
Savour of sun-baked Malbec comes through convincingly
in this blend (with 15% Grenache) to form a gently
sinewy dark fruit that will cut rich meaty dishes.

8 Tour Chapoux Bordeaux Supérieur 2015 £8.99
Firm not fierce Merlot-dominated claret with plenty of
toasty fruit (though not oaked) and developed ripeness;
stands out from the Bordeaux crowd; 13.7% alcohol.

9 Réserve des Hospitaliers Cairanne
Côtes du Rhône Villages 2015 £9.99
Waitrose claims this powerful, generous wine is aged
in new oak barriques for 15 months, a considerable
extravagance for a wine priced under a tenner. Well, I do
like it, but as much for the shining spicy darkly ripe fruits
as the toasty nuances of the wood; 13.5% alcohol and a
dependable perennial bargain.

9 Georges Duboeuf Fleurie 2015 £10.99
Delightfully jiggly juicy senior Beaujolais from the
region's biggest but impressively consistent producer; fine
purple aromas and flavours with good intensity to drink
now or keep for development. I see Duboeuf has moved
on from the jolly floral labels of old. Shame.

FRANCE

Waitrose

RED WINES

🍷 8 **Pascal Bouchard Pinot Noir 2014**   £11.99
Plump and perky strawberry-raspberry well-knit generic
burgundy; instantly likeable in spite of the sententious
apophthegm on the label 'Passion – Emotion – Tradition'.
A respectable outfit such as Bouchard should eschew this
sort of thing.

🍷 8 **Gigondas Clos la Grande Boissière 2016**   £18.99
You pay a premium for the name Gigondas among Rhône
village wines. I don't begrudge this one too much: opaque
and corrrespondingly intense in weight and spicy savour,
already mellowing though no doubt capable of long
evolution; 15% alcohol.

🍷 8 **Châteauneuf du Pape Le Relais du
         Roi 2015**   £20.99
Beguiling unoaked nicely rounding-out healthily warmly
ripe example of the famed southern Rhône classic which
has the complexity and linger you're entitled to expect
at the price; an outstanding wine even if I can't quite
identify why; 14% alcohol.

🍷 8 **Château Deyrem Valentin 2013**   £26.99
This Margaux cru bourgeois is new to me, and looked
expensive, so I tried it. Good move: inky maroon colour,
lovely sweet vanilla blueberry pie aroma and lush, long
evolving silky classic claret flavours, still grippy but
already good drinking.

RED WINES

🍷 9 Recchia Bardolino 2016   **£7.99**
The diaphanous style of Verona's most delicate red, once so fashionable, seems wildly out of step with the big flavours of today, but this scintillating cherry-bright refresher is a firm reminder that a light touch can make a memorable impression; a fine aperitif red to chill and a match for antipasto of all kinds.

🍷 9 Triade 2014   **£8.79**
No connection to Chinese organised crime here, more a virtuous teaming of three indigenous Puglian grape varieties, Negroamaro, Primitivo and Nero di Troia to make a convincingly wholesome, coffee-scented, dark and intense richly-sauced pasta red of weight and character. Lush and long, and 13.5% alcohol.

🍷 8 Villa Cafaggio Chianti Classico 2013   **£14.99**
Monster Chianti from a medieval estate once tended by Benedictines, this is deep and plush with authentic black-cherry ripeness and brisk grippiness; 13.5% alcohol. Waitrose claim it's available online only but I bought my bottle in a Dorset store for a bargain £9.99 – a third off shelf price. Worth seeking out.

🍷 8 Tommasi Arele delle Venezie 2014   **£17.99**
Occult Valpolicella offshoot is at once sweetly ripe and almond-rich and cherry-bright and perky – a fascinating and immediately likeable aperitif red or a match for saucy fish, white meats, subtle pasta flavours. Only online from Waitrose Cellar.

ITALY

RED WINES

N. ZEALAND

♈ 8 **Escarpment The Edge Pinot Noir 2016** **£14.99**
Profound Kiwi Pinot from the vine's heartland of
Martinborough is raspberry-bright, plumply ripe but
with a suitably edgy acidity and fetchingly enriched with
a degree of oak contact; 14% alcohol.

PORTUGAL

♈ 8 **Ten Mile Bridge 2015** **£7.99**
Named in honour of Lisbon's spectacular 1998-opened
Vasco da Gama road bridge, this really connects: lush,
ripe, warmly spicy Setubal from indigenous Castelão
grapes. Oddly for a wine from the world's leading cork-
growing nation, it has a screwcap.

SOUTH AFRICA

♈ 8 **Fairview Pinotage 2016** **£9.49**
Rather bashful for Pinotage, this tastes less of agreeable
tar, more of agreeable blackcurrant essence; definitely
Pinotage though, spicy but rounded, baked but lively;
14% alcohol.

♈ 8 **Rustenberg John X Merriman 2014** **£14.99**
This blood red Bordeaux-variety blend is not claret-like,
but an elegantly turned richly ripe new-oaked cassis-fruit
food red of another kind altogether; if you haven't tried
a really good Stellenbosch wine before this would be an
enlightening introduction; 14.5% alcohol.

SPAIN

♈ 8 **Waitrose Mellow and Fruity Spanish
Red 2016** **£4.99**
Ripe, just-squished-fruit style to this Campo de Borja
(neighbour to Rioja) Garnacha is fresh, healthy and
versatile as a food matcher; 13.5% alcohol.

RED WINES

SPAIN

 8　**Heredad del Rey Monastrell/Syrah**
　　　Reservada 2014　　　　　　　**£7.99**
Muscular blend from Yecla DO, grippingly dark and
spiky smoothed by an oaky ease; memorable for more
than its gaudy label and a worthy partner to charred
meat; 13.5% alc.

8　**Waitrose Rioja Crianza 2014**　　　**£9.99**
Creamy cassis fruit in the best Rioja tradition, properly
poised between keen berry brightness and vanilla richness,
13.5% alcohol.

9　**Torres Celeste Ribera del Duero**
　　Crianza 2014　　　　　　　　**£11.99**
Barrel-made pure-fruit Tinto Fino (Tempranillo) in the
lush eucalyptus-tinted slinky style of the Ribera is off-
piste for the Catalan Torres empire but bang on target;
sublime lingering creamy black fruit of finely managed
ripeness; 14.5% alcohol.

8　**La Rioja Alta Viña Arana Reserva 2009**　**£20.49**
From a distinguished bodega, a fine old Rioja in dignified
decay showing conker colour, vanilla-chocolate-cassis
aromas and fruit with a spirity edge, quite lovely and
in need of drinking up sooner rather than later; 13.5%
alcohol.

USA

8　**Dark Horse Cabernet Sauvignon 2015**　**£8.49**
It will be the California sunshine that's given this hearty
blackcurrant juice bomb its joyful exuberance; 13.5%
alcohol.

RED WINES

USA

🍷 8 **Frei Brothers Reserve Cabernet**
Sauvignon 2014   £17.99

Grown-up Sonoma Bordeaux-style wine with sweet California ripeness along with claret-like cedary savour and a slinky charm all its own. Rounded and glossy, a great partner for duck or game; 14% alcohol.

PINK WINES

FRANCE

🍷 9 **Cuvée Fleur Rosé 2016**   £4.99

Waitrose offers more than 50 different rosés and this is the one (among those I've tasted, obviously) I like best. From vineyards near the town of Béziers, it's pale, light and dry with a raspberry whiff, a lemon crispness and a cheery personality. The price is right, for rosé.

🍷 8 **Whispering Angel Côtes de Provence**
Rosé 2016   £16.99

A hell of a price to pay for a rosé, but it's as good as it gets, very pale shell pink, dry but with a saucy lift of fresh strawberry and tangy with bright acidity. And you get this verse on the label: 'In the Esclans Valley/angels whisper/if you drink this wine/you might hear them'.

GERMANY

🍷 8 **Johann Wolf Pinot Noir Rosé 2016**   £9.99

Rhine rosé is bright with strawberry colour, aroma and fruit as you might expect from Pinot Noir; this is also near-spritzily zesty and fresh and unusually interesting.

WHITE WINES

CHILE

8 Miguel Torres Las Mulas Organic
Sauvignon Blanc 2016 £9.39
Vivid citrus-bright wine from vineyards cultivated organically and tilled by implements hauled by mules; you get a fine Chilean tropical fruit salad nose and lots of corresponding interest through the fruit.

FRANCE

8 Cuvée Pêcheur 2016 £4.99
Crisp Gascon dry party white is a square deal at this price; 11.5% alcohol.

9 Waitrose Touraine Sauvignon Blanc 2016 £6.99
Impactful tangy-mineral Loire wine with lashings of gooseberry-green-grass freshness and flavours that last all the way to the citrus edge; delightful fish partner at a keen price.

8 Hen Pecked Picpoul de Pinet 2016 £7.99
Waitrose claims Picpoul grape bunches grow 'long and loose, and are ideal for hens (or "poules") to peck at, thus the name Picpoul'. This is a manifest leg-poule, but all credit to Waitrose for trying it on. This particular brand of the rightly popular seafood partner from Montpellier, by the way, is fresh, citrussy and fun.

8 Tour Chapoux Sauvignon Blanc 2016 £8.99
Gooseberries and grass to the fore in this very dry but not green Bordeaux varietal; fresh and stimulating oyster wine.

8 Cave de Turckheim Gewürztraminer 2016 £9.99
Alsace's leading co-operative makes wines for most of the UK supermarkets, but there can be variations; this one has signature lychee aroma, good heft and spice and is not too sweet.

WHITE WINES

Waitrose

FRANCE

**8 Domaine Begude Terroir 11300
Chardonnay 2016** £9.99
Well-coloured Aude wine (the number 11300 in the name
is the postcode of Limoux, nearest town to the Begude
Terroir) packing a fine balance of discreetly creamy-
oaked white-peach fruit and slaty minerality. Only in 65
stores or online.

8 Marc Dudet Pouilly-Fuissé 2013 £15.99
An exotic creamy-nutty-citrussy aroma leads the way into
this lush and mineral Mâconnais to give the full white-
burgundy effect from start to finish. Serious wine at a
reasonable price (for burgundy).

**9 Sancerre Alphonse Mellot Le
Manoir 2015** £16.49
The bottle was so heavy I nearly dropped it – one of those
18th-century style repros beloved of some marketeers –
so be warned, as this is a wine any Sancerre enthusiast
should pick up. It's a superb pebble-fresh Sauvignon of
preternatural purity with an inner richness fleetingly
evoking buttery scrambled egg; elegant and fairly
priced for one this well-made from such a fashionable
appellation.

**8 Albert Bichot Chablis 1er Cru
Fourchaume 2015** £23.99
Prices for 1er (and Grand) Cru Chablis are escalating
alarmingly. Try this one before they get out of sight. It's a
classically coloured, steely but leesily ripe (unoaked) long-
flavoured mineral pure Chardonnay in the inimitable
haunting Chablis style, already drinking well but with
years ahead of it. Only in 9 stores so look online.

WHITE WINES

FRANCE

**9 Saint-Aubin 1er Cru Sur Gamay Domaine
Gérard Thomas 2015** £23.99
Saint-Aubin might be among the humbler appellations of
Burgundy's vaunted Côte de Beaune, but it's the go-to spot
for (relatively) affordable wines genuinely representative of
the region's unique styles. This pure Chardonnay, from one
of the AC's handful of 1er Crus, is fermented and matured
in oak barrels, gorgeously coloured and rich but brightly
mineral and ideally citrus-trimmed. A fine introduction to the
world's best (well most expensive anyway) dry white wine
style for no more than the price of a bottle of half-decent gin.

6 Leitz Eins Zwei Alcohol Free Riesling 2016 £6.99
Confounding rhubarb acidity is the principal feature of
this almost recognisable Riesling by redoubtable Rhine
producer Leitz; 0% alcohol. Brave attempt.

**9 Leitz Magdalenenkreuz Riesling
Kabinett 2016** £13.99
This is more like it (see above), a fabulous racy Rheingau
Riesling in which the river of crispest apple zest flows into the
bay of lemon tang on a tide of infinitely fascinating freshness;
10% alcohol. Apologies for messing about: great German
Riesling is a lot harder to delineate than it is to enjoy.

GERMANY

**9 Willi Haag Brauneberger Juffer-Sonnenuhr
Riesling Auslese 2015** £16.99
Anxious to give credit to Waitrose for offering more
serious-quality German wines than all the other
supermarkets put together, I've carried this over from last
year as it was still in stock at my deadline. A glorious,
grapy-ripe Moselle in which the ambrosial richness is
incidental to the thrill of the Riesling rush; superb auslese
at a credible price with 7.5% alcohol. Only in a few
megastores so look online.

WHITE WINES

GREECE

🍷 8 **Hatzidakis Assyrtiko Santorini 2016** £12.99
Old friend from the Aegean's trendiest resort island is on
top form, but at a rising price. Elegant mineral flavours
given more-than-imaginary pungency by the volcanic soil
in which the vines have flourished since classical times;
13.5% alcohol.

Waitrose

ITALY

🍷 8 **Cantina Gadoro Fiano Beneventano 2016** £6.49
This particularly ripe-tasting Campania dry wine has
signature Fiano crunchy pear fruit plus suggestions of
honey and blanched almond in the depths; memorable
food white (creamy pasta, rice dishes, fish) in trim balance.

🍷 8 **Pecorino Terre di Chieti 2016** £7.99
The Pecorino vine supposedly takes its name from Italian
pecora meaning sheep because the variety prospers in
areas where sheep graze. Well, I can say this keen dry
Abruzzo white does have a grassy lushness as well as a
nice illustration of a sheep on the label. It's good. I like it.

🍷 8 **Teruzzi & Puthod Rondolino Vernaccia
di San Gimignano 2016** £8.99
The beautiful Tuscan hilltown's native dry white can be
anodyne, but this is a zesty, pleasingly pungent spin on
the modern fresh orchard-fruit style with good ripeness
and weight.

🍷 8 **Venturina Gavi del Commune di
Capriata d'Orba 2016** £9.99
In-fashion Piedmont lush dry white Gavi is surprisingly
varied in quality and price. This scores well for the
almondy richness at the centre of its green-apple fruit and
elegant citrus edge.

WHITE WINES

NEW ZEALAND

♀ 9 **The Ned Pinot Grigio 2016** £9.45
Still listed by Waitrose (among others) as a white wine,
this PG is now quite distinctly pink in hue – a coloration
more marked with each vintage, I'd aver. NZ's best-
named PG seems correspondingly a little sweeter and less
smoky than once it was, but it's as bright and stimulating
as ever, in counterpoint to the aromatic, nectarine and
sage nuances; 14% alcohol.

♀ 8 **Waitrose Villa Maria Sauvignon
    Blanc 2016** £10.49
A safe bet from one of Marlborough's most high-profile
producers – shining grassy-nettly blast-of-green-fruit
wine with a seductively ripe core to the flavours.

SLOVENIA

♀ 8 **Puklavec & Friends Sauvignon Blanc/
    Pinot Grigio 2016** £7.99
It's a bit formulaic, you might opine, to combine two of
the most popular grape varieties. But selling Slovenian
wine can't be easy, so good luck to Puklavec and friends,
who Waitrose have been supporting for years. The wine's
good, by the way, crisply fresh with lemon and grapefruit
twang and note of smoky spice.

SOUTH AFRICA

♀ 8 **The Waterfront Chardonnay/Viognier 2016** £7.99
Broad-appeal blend from the Breede Valley in Western
Cape has the ripe white fruit aromas and peachy-apricot
fruits in nice balance; artful and alluring.

Waitrose

WHITE WINES

SOUTH AFRICA

🍷 **10** **Springfield Estate Special Cuvée Sauvignon Blanc 2016** £10.99

I appreciate Waitrose's own observation that this product of a very well-run family estate in Robertson is in a style 'between the Loire's cool flintiness and New Zealand's tropical fruit'. And there's the Cape's problem with Sauvignon: it lacks identity. Or does it? Try this: it's crackingly keen and lushly juicy, in its very own way. World-class wine.

🍷 **8** **David Sadie Chenin Blanc 2015** £24.99

Lavishly coloured dry-finishing wine has what I've noted as 'grown-up' flavours of Chenin Blanc, tropical, honeyed and lingering with an ideal citrus balance; 13.5% alcohol. Quite expensive and in 6 stores only so look online.

🍷 **9** **Waitrose Spanish Dry White Aromatic and Citrus White** £4.99

A very fair description is enshrined in the name of this excellent anonymous house wine – a zestily fresh and apple-crisp blend of (recent) vintages of humble Airen grapes with some Sauvignon Blanc and Verdejo.

SPAIN

🍷 **8** **Rioja Arnegui Viura Blanco 2016** £7.99

Note to seekers-of old-fashioned (and fast-disappearing) oxidative white Rioja: this isn't one. It's good floral Viura, but made in the modern bracing style. More like a Rueda than a Rioja, you might aver.

🍷 **8** **Tuna Club Verdejo/Sauvignon Blanc 2016** £7.99

In case you're unaware of the sea-fresh style today's Spanish winemakers like to fashion from Verdejo and Sauvignon grapes, the name Tuna Club is possibly intended to put you in the picture. Whatever, this is a well-coloured and nicely briny dry wine from quite a long way inland from Valencia. Nice, natch, with fish!

WHITE WINES

**9 Waitrose Viña Taboexa Albariño Rias
Baixas 2016**   £8.29
This really is a seaside wine, from Galicia's wild Atlantic
coast, jangling with tangy white flavours, ocean fresh and
finely finished with a lingering citrus acidity; it's ripe, too,
with good sapid intensity, assertive enough to stand up to
every kind of fishy flavour.

8 Cune Barrel-Fermented Rioja Blanco 2016 £10.99
New American oak casks are used here to make this very
discreetly creamy lively dry white Rioja with nothing
oxidative about it whatsoever. Fresh, modern, dependable.

8 Sandiford Road Pinot Grigio 2016   £8.99
Californian PG! I gather the clone of the vine at Sandiford
Road in the Central Valley is unique to the estate, and it
does have its own pleasing floral and limey aromas and
softly vegetal style; hard to pin down but certainly fresh
and fun. PG fans should try at once.

**8 Frei Brothers Reserve Chardonnay
Russian River Valley 2015**   £17.99
Sweet toffee heart to this gently minerally and really quite
rich dry Californian wine featuring likeable coconut oak
and lots of ripe beguilement; 14% alcohol.

FORTIFIED WINES

9 Waitrose Oloroso Réal Sherry   £9.99
Bronze colour no darker than its amontillado or palo
cortado counterparts, but this superb oloroso ('fragrant')
sherry has a palpably charred edge to its darkly pungent
preserved-fruit flavours; extraordinary dry-finishing
sherry to sip with cheese, nuts, chocolate, olives, you
name it; 20% alcohol.

FORTIFIED WINES

8 Waitrose Don Gaspar Amontillado Sherry £9.99
Fine bronze gold colour, spirity sweet-nut nose but this is
a naturally dry sherry, though laden with conserved-fruit
richness and heady ripeness; 19% alcohol.

8 Waitrose Torre del Oro Palo Cortado Sherry £9.99
Bronze colour, pungent raisiny-figgy aromas and fruit in
fine balance finishing briskly dry; 19% alcohol.

9 Tio Pepe En Rama Sherry £15.00
Esoteric fino-type sherry made exclusively from free-run
and first-press juice has a green-gold colour, pungent
orange-pith and smoky fino aroma and thrilling dry
tangy-white-nutty fresh wild flavours; 15% alcohol.
Serve well chilled. In 20 stores only so look online.

SPARKLING WINES

9 Leckford Estate Brut 2013 £24.99
More garlands for English fizz. This Chardonnay-Pinots
blend from Waitrose's Hampshire vineyard is a fine
sparkler but not like champagne; its generous fullness
feels as if it derives from natural fruit ripeness rather than
sugary dosage. Which is unfair to good champagne, of
course, but do try this.

8 Cuvée Royale Crémant de Limoux Brut £11.99
Creamily foaming (as the description crémant suggests)
Pyrenees sparkler with rich colour and inviting digestive
biscuit nose followed up by mellow Chardonnay fruit
lifted by an efficient citrus acidity; old-fashioned and
none the worse for that.

SPARKLING WINES

8 **Waitrose Champagne Blanc de Noirs Brut** £21.99
This pure Pinot Noir has an inviting bakery nose and
mellow fruit, very easy to like.

10 **Waitrose Special Reserve Champagne**
Vintage Brut 2005 £24.99
I rated this fabulous mature champagne at 10 points in
last year's edition and then couldn't find a bottle of it
in any store. Now it's reappeared at the 2017 tasting. I
believe it tastes even better, a rare buttered-toast-aroma,
mellow ripe deep fruit flavours, glorious fun – and the
price seems a giveaway. Seek it out.

9 **Louis Roederer Cristal Brut 2009** £160.00
Last year I tasted the 2007 Cristal and liked it. This year
it's the 2009 and I like it even better. Do I get fruitcake
as well as brioche on the luxuriant nose? It's quite pale
in colour but full of mellowness and good intentions.
Amazingly, this is stocked in 189 stores.

8 **San Leo Prosecco Brut** £10.49
It's almost dry, not quite, with cheery elderflower pong
and sweet-pear froth in a fresh and friendly style; 11%
alcohol.

FRANCE

ITALY

—Making the most of it—

There has always been a lot of nonsense talked about the correct ways to serve wine. Red wine, we are told, should be opened and allowed to 'breathe' before pouring. White wine should be chilled. Wine doesn't go with soup, tomatoes or chocolate. You know the sort of thing.

It would all be simply laughable except that these daft conventions do make so many potential wine lovers nervous about the simple ritual of opening a bottle and sharing it around. Here is a short and opinionated guide to the received wisdom.

Breathing

Simply uncorking a wine for an hour or two before you serve it will make absolutely no difference to the way it tastes. However, if you wish to warm up an icy bottle of red by placing it near (never on) a radiator or fire, do remove the cork first. As the wine warms, even very slightly, it gives off gas, which will spoil the flavour if it cannot escape.

Chambré-ing

One of the more florid terms in the wine vocabulary. The idea is that red wine should be at the same temperature as the room (chambre) you're going to drink it in. In fairness, it makes sense – although the term harks back to the days when the only people who drank wine were those who could afford to keep it in the freezing cold vaulted cellars beneath their houses. The ridiculously high temperatures to which some homes are raised by central heating systems today are really far too warm for wine. But presumably those who live in such circumstances do so out of choice, and will prefer their wine to be similarly overheated.

Chilling

Drink your white wine as cold as you like. It's certainly true that good whites are at their best at a cool rather than at an icy temperature, but cheap and characterless wines can be improved immeasurably if they are cold enough – the anaesthetising effect of the temperature removes all sense of taste. Pay no attention to notions that red wine should not be served cool. There are plenty of lightweight reds that will respond very well to an hour in the fridge.

Corked wine

Wine trade surveys reveal that far too many bottles are in no fit state to be sold. The villain is very often cited as the cork. Cut from the bark of cork-oak trees cultivated for the purpose in Portugal and Spain, these natural stoppers have done sterling service for 200 years, but now face a crisis of confidence among wine producers. A diseased or damaged cork can make the wine taste stale because air has penetrated, or musty-mushroomy due to TCA, an infection of the raw material. These faults in wine, known as 'corked' or 'corky', should be immediately obvious, even in the humblest bottle, so you should return the bottle to the supplier and demand a refund.

Today, more and more wine producers are opting to close their bottles with polymer bungs. Some are designed to resemble the 'real thing' while others come in a rather disorienting range of colours – including black. While these things can be a pain to extract, there seems to be no evidence they do any harm to the wine. Don't 'lay down' bottles closed with polymer. The potential effects of years of contact with the plastic are yet to be scientifically established.

The same goes for screwcaps. These do have the merit of obviating the struggle with the corkscrew, but prolonged contact of the plastic liner with the wine might not be a good idea.

Corkscrews

The best kind of corkscrew is the 'waiter's friend' type. It looks like a pen-knife, unfolding a 'worm' (the helix or screw) and a lever device which, after the worm has been driven into the cork (try to centre it) rests on the lip of the bottle and enables you to withdraw the cork with minimal effort. Some have two-stage lips to facilitate the task. These devices are cheaper and longer-lasting than any of the more elaborate types, and are equally effective at withdrawing polymer bungs – which can be hellishly difficult to unwind from Teflon-coated 'continuous' corkscrews like the Screwpull.

Decanting

There are two views on the merits of decanting wines. The prevailing one seems to be that it is pointless and even pretentious. The other is that it can make real improvements in the way a wine tastes and is definitely worth the trouble.

Scientists, not usually much exercised by the finer nuances of wine, will tell you that exposure to the air causes wine to 'oxidise' – take in oxygen molecules that will quite quickly initiate the process of turning wine into vinegar – and anyone who has tasted a 'morning-after' glass of wine will no doubt vouch for this.

But the fact that wine does oxidise is a genuine clue to the reality of the effects of exposure to air. Shut inside its bottle, a young wine is very much a live substance, jumping with natural, but mysterious, compounds that can cause all sorts of strange taste sensations. But by exposing the wine to air these effects are markedly reduced.

In wines that spend longer in the bottle, the influence of these factors diminishes, in a process called 'reduction'. In red wines, the hardness of tannin – the natural preservative imparted into wine from the grape skins – gradually reduces, just as the raw purple colour darkens to ruby and later to orangey-brown.

I believe there is less reason for decanting old wines than new, unless the old wine has thrown a deposit and needs carefully to be poured off it. And in some light-bodied wines, such as older Rioja, decanting is probably a bad idea because it can accelerate oxidation all too quickly.

As to actual experiments, I have carried out several of my own, with wines opened in advance or wines decanted compared to the same wines just opened and poured, and my own unscientific judgement is that big, young, alcoholic reds can certainly be improved by aeration.

Washing glasses

If your wine glasses are of any value to you, don't put them in the dishwasher. Over time, they'll craze from the heat of the water. And they will not emerge in the glitteringly pristine condition suggested by the pictures on some detergent packets. For genuinely perfect glasses that will stay that way, wash them in hot soapy water, rinse with clean, hot water and dry immediately with a glass cloth kept exclusively for this purpose. Sounds like fanaticism, but if you take your wine seriously, you'll see there is sense in it.

Keeping wine

How long can you keep an opened bottle of wine before it goes downhill? Not long. A re-corked bottle with just a glassful out of it should stay fresh until the day after, but if there is a lot of air inside the bottle, the wine will oxidise, turning progressively stale and sour. Wine 'saving' devices that allow you to withdraw the air from the bottle via a punctured, self-sealing rubber stopper are variably effective, but don't expect these to keep a wine fresh for more than a couple of re-openings. A crafty method of keeping a half-finished bottle is to decant it, via a funnel, into a clean half bottle and recork.

Storing wine

Supermarket labels always seem to advise that 'this wine should be consumed within one year of purchase'. I think this is a wheeze to persuade customers to drink it up quickly and come back for more. Many of the more robust red wines are likely to stay in good condition for much more than one year, and plenty will actually improve with age. On the other hand, it is a sensible axiom that inexpensive dry white wines are better the younger they are. If you do intend to store wines for longer than a few weeks, do pay heed to the conventional wisdom that bottles are best stored in low, stable temperatures, preferably in the dark. Bottles closed with conventional corks should be laid on their side lest the corks dry out for lack of contact with the wine. But one of the notable advantages of the new closures now proliferating is that if your wine comes with a polymer 'cork' or a screwcap, you can safely store it upright.

Wine and food

Wine is made to be drunk with food, but some wines go better with particular dishes than others. It is no coincidence that Italian wines, characterised by soft, cherry fruit and a clean, mouth-drying finish, go so well with the sticky delights of pasta.

But it's personal taste rather than national associations that should determine the choice of wine with food. And if you prefer a black-hearted Argentinian Malbec to a brambly Italian Barbera with your Bolognese, that's fine.

The conventions that have grown up around wine and food pairings do make some sense, just the same. I was thrilled to learn in the early days of my drinking career that sweet, dessert wines can go well with strong blue cheese. As I don't much like puddings, but love sweet wines, I was eager to test this match – and I'm here to tell you that it works very well indeed as the end-piece to a grand meal in which there is cheese as well as pud on offer.

Red wine and cheese are supposed to be a natural match, but I'm not so sure. Reds can taste awfully tinny with soft cheeses such as Brie and Camembert, and even worse with goat's cheese. A really extravagant, yellow Australian Chardonnay will make a better match. Hard cheeses such as Cheddar and the wonderful Old Amsterdam (top-of-the-market Gouda) are better with reds.

And then there's the delicate issue of fish. Red wine is supposed to be a no-no. This might well be true of grilled and wholly unadorned white fish, such as sole or a delicate dish of prawns, scallops or crab. But what about oven-roasted monkfish or a substantial winter-season fish pie? An edgy red will do very well indeed, and provide much comfort for those many among us who simply prefer to drink red wine with food, and white wine on its own.

It is very often the method by which dishes are prepared, rather than their core ingredients, that determines which wine will work best. To be didactic, I would always choose Beaujolais or summer-fruit-style reds such as those from Pinot Noir grapes to go with a simple roast chicken. But if the bird is cooked as coq au vin with a hefty wine sauce, I would plump for a much more assertive red.

Some sauces, it is alleged, will overwhelm all wines. Salsa and curry come to mind. I have carried out a number of experiments into this great issue of our time, in my capacity as consultant to a company that specialises in supplying wines to Asian restaurants. One discovery I have made is that forcefully fruity dry white wines with keen acidity can go very well indeed even with fairly incendiary dishes. Sauvignon Blanc with Madras? Give it a try!

I'm also convinced, however, that some red wines will stand up very well to a bit of heat. The marvellously robust reds of Argentina made from Malbec grapes are good partners to Mexican chilli-hot recipes and salsa dishes. The dry, tannic edge to these wines provides a good counterpoint to the inflammatory spices in the food.

Some foods are supposedly impossible to match with wine. Eggs and chocolate are among the prime offenders. And yet, legendary cook Elizabeth David's best-selling autobiography was entitled *An Omelette and a Glass of Wine*, and the affiliation between chocolates and champagne is an unbreakable one. Taste is, after all, that most personally governed of all senses. If your choice is a boiled egg washed down with a glass of claret, who is to dictate otherwise?

What wine
——————— words mean ———————

Wine labels are getting crowded. It's mostly thanks to the unending torrent of new regulation. Lately, for example, the European Union has decided that all wines sold within its borders must display a health warning: 'Contains Sulphites'. All wines are made with the aid of preparations containing sulphur to combat diseases in the vineyards and bacterial infections in the winery. You can't make wine without sulphur. Even 'organic' wines are made with it. But some people are sensitive to the traces of sulphur in some wines, so we must all be informed of the presence of this hazardous material.

That's the way it is. And it might not be long before some even sterner warnings will be added about another ingredient in wine. Alcohol is the new tobacco, as the regulators see it, and in the near future we can look forward to some stern admonishments about the effects of alcohol. In the meantime, the mandatory information on every label includes the quantity, alcoholic strength and country of origin, along with the name of the producer. The region will be specified, vaguely on wines from loosely regulated countries such as Australia, and precisely on wines from over-regulated countries such as France. Wines from 'classic' regions of Europe – Bordeaux, Chianti, Rioja and so on – are mostly labelled according to their location rather than their constituent grape varieties. If it says Sancerre, it's taken as read that you either know it's made with Sauvignon Blanc grapes, or don't care.

Wines from just about everywhere else make no such assumptions. If a New Zealand wine is made from Sauvignon Blanc grapes, you can be sure the label will say so. This does quite neatly represent the gulf between the two worlds of winemaking. In traditional European regions, it's the place, the vineyard, that mostly determines the character of the wines. The French call it *terroir*, to encapsulate not just the lie of the land and the soil conditions but the wild variations in the weather from year to year as well. The grapes are merely the medium through which the timeless mysteries of the deep earth are translated into the ineffable glories of the wine, adjusted annually according to the vagaries of climate, variable moods of the winemaker, and who knows what else.

In the less arcane vineyards of the New World, the grape is definitely king. In hot valleys such as the Barossa (South Australia) or the Maipo (Chile), climate is relatively predictable and the soil conditions are managed by irrigation. It's the fruit that counts, and the style of the wine is determined by the variety – soft, spicy Shiraz; peachy, yellow Chardonnay and so on.

The main purpose of this glossary is, consequently, to give short descriptions of the 'classic' wines, including the names of the grapes they are made from, and of the 70-odd distinct grape varieties that make most of the world's wines. As well as these very brief descriptions, I have included equally shortened summaries of the regions and appellations of the better-known wines, along with some of the local terms used to indicate style and alleged qualities.

Finally, I have tried to explain in simple and rational terms the peculiar words I use in trying to convey the characteristics of wines described. 'Delicious' might need no further qualification, but the likes of 'bouncy', 'green' and 'liquorous' probably do.

A

abboccato – Medium-dry white wine style. Italy, especially Orvieto.

AC – *See* Appellation d'Origine Contrôlée.

acidity – To be any good, every wine must have the right level of acidity. It gives wine the element of dryness or sharpness it needs to prevent cloying sweetness or dull wateriness. If there is too much acidity, wine tastes raw or acetic (vinegary). Winemakers strive to create balanced acidity – either by cleverly controlling the natural processes, or by adding sugar and acid to correct imbalances.

aftertaste – The flavour that lingers in the mouth after swallowing the wine.

Aglianico – Black grape variety of southern Italy. It has romantic associations. When the ancient Greeks first colonised Italy in the seventh century BC, it was with the prime purpose of planting it as a vineyard (the Greek name for Italy was *Oenotria* – land of cultivated vines). The name for the vines the Greeks brought with them was Ellenico (as in Hellas, Greece), from which Aglianico is the modern rendering. To return to the point, these ancient vines, especially in the arid volcanic landscapes of Basilicata and Cilento, produce excellent dark, earthy and highly distinctive wines. A name to look out for.

Agriculture biologique – On French wine labels, an indication that the wine has been made by organic methods.

Albariño – White grape variety of Spain that makes intriguingly perfumed fresh and spicy dry wines, especially in esteemed Rias Baixas region.

alcohol – The alcohol levels in wines are expressed in terms of alcohol by volume ('abv'), that is, the percentage of the volume of the wine that is common, or ethyl, alcohol. A typical wine at 12 per cent abv is thus 12 parts alcohol and, in effect, 88 parts fruit juice.

The question of how much alcohol we can drink without harming ourselves in the short or long term is an impossible one to answer, but there is more or less general agreement among scientists that small amounts of alcohol are good for us, even if the only evidence of this is actuarial – the fact that mortality statistics show teetotallers live significantly shorter lives than moderate drinkers. The Department of Health now declares there is no safe level of alcohol consumption, but continues to advise that drinkers should not exceed a weekly number of 'units' of alcohol. A unit is 10ml of pure alcohol, the quantity contained in about half a 175ml glass of wine with 12 per cent alcohol. From 1995, the advisory limit on weekly units was 28 for men and 21 for women. This was reduced in 2016 to 14 for men and women alike.

Alentejo – Wine region of southern Portugal (immediately north of the Algarve), with a fast-improving reputation, especially for sappy, keen reds from local grape varieties including Aragones, Castelão and Trincadeira.

Almansa – DO winemaking region of Spain inland from Alicante, making great-value red wines.

Alsace – France's easternmost wine-producing region lies between the Vosges Mountains and the River Rhine, with Germany beyond. These conditions make for the production of some of the world's most delicious and fascinating white wines, always sold under the name of their constituent grapes. Pinot Blanc is the most affordable – and is well worth looking out for. The 'noble' grape varieties of the region are Gewürztraminer, Muscat, Riesling and Pinot Gris and they are always made on a single-variety basis. The richest, most exotic wines are those from individual *grand cru* vineyards, which are named on the label. Some *vendange tardive* (late harvest) wines are made, but tend to be expensive. All the wines are sold in tall, slim green bottles known as flûtes that closely resemble those of the Mosel, and the names of producers and grape varieties are often German too, so it is widely assumed that Alsace wines are German in style, if not in nationality. But this is not the case in either particular. Alsace wines are dry and quite unique in character – and definitely French.

Amarone – Style of red wine made in Valpolicella, Italy. Specially selected grapes are held back from the harvest and stored for several months to dry them out. They are then pressed and fermented into a highly concentrated speciality dry wine. Amarone means 'bitter', describing the dry style of the flavour.

amontillado – *See* sherry.

aperitif – If a wine is thus described, I believe it will give more pleasure before a meal than with one. Crisp, low-alcohol German wines and other delicately flavoured whites (including many dry Italians) are examples.

Appellation d'Origine Contrôlée – Commonly abbreviated to AC or AOC, this is the system under which quality wines are defined in France. About a third of the country's vast annual output qualifies, and there are more than 400 distinct AC zones. The declaration of an AC on the label signifies that the wine meets standards concerning location of vineyards and wineries, grape varieties and limits on harvest per hectare, methods of cultivation and vinification, and alcohol content. Wines are inspected and tasted by state-appointed committees. The one major aspect of any given wine that an AC cannot guarantee is that you will like it – but it certainly improves the chances.

Appellation d'Origine Protégée (AOP) – Under European Union rule changes, the AOC system is gradually transforming into AOP. In effect, it will mean little more than the exchange of 'controlled' with 'protected' on labels. One quirk of the new rules is that makers of AOP wines will be able to name the constituent grape variety or varieties on their labels, if they so wish.

Apulia – Anglicised name for Puglia.

Aragones – Synonym in Portugal, especially in the Alentejo region, for the Tempranillo grape variety of Spain.

Ardèche – Region of southern France to the west of the Rhône valley, home to a good vin de pays zone known as the Coteaux de L'Ardèche. Lots of decent-value reds from Syrah grapes, and some, less interesting, dry whites.

Arneis – White grape variety of Piedmont, north-west Italy. Makes dry whites with a certain almondy richness at often-inflated prices.

Assyrtiko – White grape variety of Greece now commonly named on dry white wines, sometimes of great quality, from the mainland and islands.

Asti – Town and major winemaking centre in Piedmont, Italy. The sparkling (spumante) sweet wines made from Moscato grapes are inexpensive and often delicious. Typical alcohol level is a modest 5 to 7 per cent.

attack – In wine tasting, the first impression made by the wine in the mouth.

Auslese – German wine-quality designation. *See* QmP.

B

Baga – Black grape variety indigenous to Portugal. Makes famously concentrated, juicy reds that get their deep colour from the grape's particularly thick skins. Look out for this name, now quite frequently quoted as the varietal on Portuguese wine labels. Often very good value for money.

balance – A big word in the vocabulary of wine tasting. Respectable wine must get two key things right: lots of fruitiness from the sweet grape juice, and plenty of acidity so the sweetness is 'balanced' with the crispness familiar in good dry whites and the dryness that marks out good reds. Some wines are noticeably 'well balanced' in that they have memorable fruitiness and the clean, satisfying 'finish' (last flavour in the mouth) that ideal acidity imparts.

Barbera – Black grape variety originally of Piedmont in Italy. Most commonly seen as Barbera d'Asti, the vigorously fruity red wine made around Asti – once better known for sweet sparkling Asti Spumante. Barbera grapes are now being grown in South America, often producing a sleeker, smoother style than at home in Italy.

Bardolino – Once fashionable, light red wine DOC of Veneto, north-west Italy. Bardolino is made principally from Corvina Veronese grapes plus Rondinella, Molinara and Negrara. Best wines are supposed to be those labelled Bardolino Superiore, a DOCG created in 2002. This classification closely specifies the permissible grape varieties and sets the alcohol level at a minimum of 12 per cent.

Barossa Valley – Famed vineyard region north of Adelaide, Australia, produces hearty reds principally from Shiraz, Cabernet Sauvignon and Grenache grapes, plus plenty of lush white wine from Chardonnay. Also known for limey, long-lived, mineral dry whites from Riesling grapes.

barrique – Barrel in French. *En barrique* on a wine label signifies the wine has been matured in oak.

Beaujolais – Unique red wines from the southern reaches of Burgundy, France, are made from Gamay grapes. Beaujolais nouveau, now deeply unfashionable, provides a friendly introduction to the bouncy, red-fruit style of the wine, but for the authentic experience, go for Beaujolais Villages, from the region's better, northern vineyards. There are ten AC zones within this northern sector making wines under their own names. Known as the *crus*, these are Brouilly, Chénas, Chiroubles, Côte de Brouilly, Fleurie, Juliénas, Morgon, Moulin à Vent, Regnié and St Amour and produce most of the best wines of the region. Prices are higher than those for Beaujolais Villages, but by no means always justifiably so.

Beaumes de Venise – Village near Châteauneuf du Pape in France's Rhône valley, famous for sweet and alcoholic wine from Muscat grapes. Delicious, grapey wines. A small number of growers also make strong (sometimes rather tough) red wines under the village name.

Beaune – One of the two winemaking centres (the other is Nuits St Georges) at the heart of Burgundy in France. Three of the region's humbler appellations take the name of the town: Côtes de Beaune, Côtes de Beaune Villages and Hautes Côtes de Beaune. Wines made under these ACs are often, but by no means always, good value for money.

berry fruit – Some red wines deliver a burst of flavour in the mouth that corresponds to biting into a newly picked berry – strawberry, blackberry, etc. So a wine described as having berry fruit (by this writer, anyway) has freshness, liveliness and immediate appeal.

bianco – White wine, Italy.

Bical – White grape variety principally of Dão region of northern Portugal. Not usually identified on labels, because most of it goes into inexpensive sparkling wines. Can make still wines of very refreshing crispness.

biodynamics – A cultivation method taking the organic approach several steps further. Biodynamic winemakers plant and tend their vineyards according to a date and time calendar 'in harmony' with the movements of the planets. Some of France's best-known wine estates subscribe, and many more are going that way. It might all sound bonkers, but it's salutary to learn that biodynamics is based on principles first described by a very eminent man, the Austrian educationist Rudolph Steiner.

bite – In wine tasting, the impression on the palate of a wine with plenty of acidity and, often, tannin.

blanc – White wine, France.

blanc de blancs – White wine from white grapes, France. May seem to be stating the obvious, but some white wines (e.g. champagne) are made, partially or entirely, from black grapes.

blanc de noirs – White wine from black grapes, France. Usually sparkling (especially champagne) made from black Pinot Meunier and Pinot Noir grapes, with no Chardonnay or other white varieties.

blanco – White wine, Spain and Portugal.

Blauer Zweigelt – Black grape variety of Austria, making a large proportion of the country's red wines, some of excellent quality.

Bobal – Black grape variety mostly of south-eastern Spain. Thick skin is good for colour and juice contributes acidity to blends.

bodega – In Spain, a wine producer or wine shop.

Bonarda – Black grape variety of northern Italy. Now more widely planted in Argentina, where it makes rather elegant red wines, often representing great value.

botrytis – Full name, *botrytis cinerea*, is that of a beneficent fungus that can attack ripe grape bunches late in the season, shrivelling the berries to a gruesome-looking mess, which yields concentrated juice of prized sweetness. Cheerfully known as 'noble rot', this fungus is actively encouraged by winemakers in regions as diverse as Sauternes (in Bordeaux), Monbazillac (in Bergerac), the Rhine and Mosel valleys, Hungary's Tokaji region and South Australia to make ambrosial dessert wines.

bouncy – The feel in the mouth of a red wine with young, juicy fruitiness. Good Beaujolais is bouncy, as are many north-west-Italian wines from Barbera and Dolcetto grapes.

Bourgogne Grand Ordinaire – Former AC of Burgundy, France. *See* Coteaux Bourguignons.

Bourgueil – Appellation of Loire Valley, France. Long-lived red wines from Cabernet Franc grapes.

briary – In wine tasting, associated with the flavours of fruit from prickly bushes such as blackberries.

brûlé – Pleasant burnt-toffee taste or smell, as in crème brûlée.

brut – Driest style of sparkling wine. Originally French, for very dry champagnes specially developed for the British market, but now used for sparkling wines from all round the world.

Buzet – Little-seen AC of south-west France overshadowed by Bordeaux but producing some characterful ripe reds.

C

Cabardès – AC for red and rosé wines from area north of Carcassonne, Aude, France. Principally Cabernet Sauvignon and Merlot grapes.

Cabernet Franc – Black grape variety originally of France. It makes the light-bodied and keenly edged red wines of the Loire Valley – such as Chinon and Saumur. And it is much grown in Bordeaux, especially in the appellation of St Emilion. Also now planted in Argentina, Australia and North America. Wines, especially in the Loire, are characterised by a leafy, sappy style and bold fruitiness. Most are best enjoyed young.

Cabernet Sauvignon – Black (or, rather, blue) grape variety now grown in virtually every wine-producing nation. When perfectly ripened, the grapes are smaller than many other varieties and have particularly thick skins. This means that when pressed, Cabernet grapes have a high proportion of skin to juice – and that makes for wine with lots of colour and tannin. In Bordeaux, the grape's traditional home, the grandest Cabernet-based wines have always been known as *vins de garde* (wines to keep) because they take years, even decades, to evolve as the effect of all that skin extraction preserves the fruit all the way to magnificent maturity. But in today's impatient world, these grapes are exploited in modern winemaking techniques to produce the sublime flavours of mature Cabernet without having to hang around for lengthy periods awaiting maturation. While there's nothing like a fine, ten-year-old claret (and nothing quite as expensive), there are many excellent Cabernets from around the world that amply illustrate this grape's characteristics. Classic smells and flavours include blackcurrants, cedar wood, chocolate, tobacco – even violets.

Cahors – An AC of the Lot Valley in south-west France once famous for 'black wine'. This was a curious concoction of straightforward wine mixed with a soupy must, made by boiling up new-pressed juice to concentrate it (through evaporation) before fermentation. The myth is still perpetuated that Cahors wine continues to be made in this way, but production on this basis actually ceased 150 years ago. Cahors today is no stronger, or blacker, than the wines of neighbouring appellations.

Cairanne – Village of the appellation collectively known as the Côtes du Rhône in southern France. Cairanne is one of several villages entitled to put their name on the labels of wines made within their AC boundary, and the appearance of this name is quite reliably an indicator of a very good wine indeed.

Calatayud – DO (quality wine zone) near Zaragoza in the Aragon region of northern Spain where they're making some astonishingly good wines at bargain prices, mainly reds from Garnacha and Tempranillo grapes. These are the varieties that go into the polished and oaky wines of Rioja, but in Calatayud, the wines are dark, dense and decidedly different.

Cannonau – Black grape native to Sardinia by name, but in fact the same variety as the ubiquitous Grenache of France (and Garnacha of Spain).

cantina sociale – *See* co-op.

Carignan – Black grape variety of Mediterranean France. It is rarely identified on labels, but is a major constituent of wines from the southern Rhône and Languedoc-Roussillon regions. Known as Carignano in Italy and Cariñena in Spain.

Cariñena – A region of north-east Spain, south of Navarra, known for substantial reds, as well as the Spanish name for the Carignan grape (*qv*).

Carmenère – Black grape variety once widely grown in Bordeaux but abandoned due to cultivation problems. Lately revived in South America where it is producing fine wines, sometimes with echoes of Bordeaux.

cassis – As a tasting note, signifies a wine that has a noticeable blackcurrant-concentrate flavour or smell. Much associated with the Cabernet Sauvignon grape.

Castelao – Portuguese black grape variety. Same as Periquita.

Catarratto – White grape variety of Sicily. In skilled hands it can make anything from keen, green-fruit dry whites to lush, oaked super-ripe styles. Also used for Marsala.

cat's pee – In tasting notes, a mildly jocular reference to a certain style of Sauvignon Blanc wine.

cava – The sparkling wine of Spain. Most originates in Catalonia, but the Denominación de Origen (DO) guarantee of authenticity is open to producers in many regions of the country. Much cava is very reasonably priced even though it is made by the same method as champagne – second fermentation in bottle, known in Spain as the *método clásico*.

CdR – Côtes du Rhône.

Cépage – Grape variety, French. 'Cépage Merlot' on a label simply means the wine is made largely or exclusively from Merlot grapes.

Chablis – Northernmost AC of France's Burgundy region. Its dry white wines from Chardonnay grapes are known for their fresh and steely style, but the best wines also age very gracefully into complex classics.

Chambourcin – Sounds like a cream cheese but it's a relatively modern (1963) French hybrid black grape that makes some good non-appellation lightweight-but-concentrated reds in the Loire Valley and now some heftier versions in Australia.

Chardonnay – The world's most popular grape variety. Said to originate from the village of Chardonnay in the Mâconnais region of southern Burgundy, the vine is now planted in every wine-producing nation. Wines are commonly characterised by generous colour and sweet-apple smell, but styles range from lean and sharp to opulently rich. Australia started the craze for oaked Chardonnay, the gold-coloured, super-ripe, buttery 'upfront' wines that are a caricature of lavish and outrageously expensive burgundies such as Meursault and Puligny-Montrachet. Rich to the point of egginess, these Aussie pretenders are now giving way to a sleeker, more minerally style with much less oak presence – if any at all. California and Chile, New Zealand and South Africa are competing hard to imitate the Burgundian style, and Australia's success in doing so.

Châteauneuf du Pape – Famed appellation centred on a picturesque village of the southern Rhône valley in France where in the 1320s French Pope Clement V had a splendid new château built for himself as a country retreat amidst his vineyards. The red wines of the AC, which can be made from 13 different grape varieties but principally Grenache, Syrah and Mourvèdre, are regarded as the best of the southern Rhône and have become rather expensive – but they can be sensationally good. Expensive white wines are also made.

Chenin Blanc – White grape variety of the Loire Valley, France. Now also grown farther afield, especially in South Africa. Makes dry, soft white wines and also rich, sweet styles. Sadly, many low-cost Chenin wines are bland and uninteresting.

cherry – In wine tasting, either a pale red colour or, more commonly, a smell or flavour akin to the sun-warmed, bursting sweet ripeness of cherries. Many Italian wines, from lightweights such as Bardolino and Valpolicella to serious Chianti, have this character. 'Black cherry' as a description is often used of Merlot wines – meaning they are sweet but have a firmness of flavour associated with the thicker skins of black cherries.

Cinsault – Black grape variety of southern France, where it is invariably blended with others in wines of all qualities ranging from vin de pays to the pricy reds of Châteauneuf du Pape. Also much planted in South Africa. The effect in wine is to add keen aromas (sometimes compared with turpentine!) and softness to the blend. The name is often spelt Cinsaut.

Clape, La – A small *cru* (defined quality-vineyard area) within the Coteaux du Languedoc where the growers make some seriously delicious red wines, mainly from Carignan, Grenache and Syrah grapes. A name worth looking out for on labels from the region.

claret – The red wine of Bordeaux, France. It comes from Latin *clarus*, meaning 'clear', recalling a time when the red wines of the region were much lighter in colour than they are now.

clarete – On Spanish labels indicates a pale-coloured red wine. Tinto signifies a deeper hue.

classed growth – English translation of French *cru classé* describes a group of 60 individual wine estates in the Médoc district of Bordeaux, which in 1855 were granted this new status on the basis that their wines were the most expensive at that time. The classification was a promotional wheeze to attract attention to the Bordeaux stand at that year's Great Exhibition in Paris. Amazingly, all of the 60 wines concerned are still in production and most still occupy more or less their original places in the pecking order price-wise. The league was divided up into five divisions from *Premier Grand Cru Classé* (just four wines originally, with one promoted in 1971 – the only change ever made to the classification) to *Cinquième Grand Cru Classé*. Other regions of Bordeaux, notably Graves and St Emilion, have since imitated Médoc and introduced their own rankings of *cru classé* estates.

classic – An overused term in every respect – wine descriptions being no exception. In this book, the word is used to describe a very good wine of its type. So, a 'classic' Cabernet Sauvignon is one that is recognisably and admirably characteristic of that grape.

Classico – Under Italy's wine laws, this word appended to the name of a DOC zone has an important significance. The classico wines of the region can only be made from vineyards lying in the best-rated areas, and wines thus labelled (e.g. Chianti Classico, Soave Classico, Valpolicella Classico) can be reliably counted on to be a cut above the rest.

Colombard – White grape variety of southern France. Once employed almost entirely for making the wine that is distilled for armagnac and cognac brandies, but lately restored to varietal prominence in the Vin de Pays des Côtes de Gascogne where high-tech wineries turn it into a fresh and crisp, if unchallenging, dry wine at a budget price. But beware, cheap Colombard (especially from South Africa) can still be very dull.

Conca de Barbera – Winemaking region of Catalonia, Spain.

co-op – Very many of France's good-quality, inexpensive wines are made by co-operatives. These are wine-producing factories whose members, and joint-owners, are local *vignerons* (vine growers). Each year they sell their harvests to the co-op for turning into branded wines. In Italy, co-op wines can be identified by the words *Cantina Sociale* on the label and in Germany by the term *Winzergenossenschaft*.

Corbières – A name to look out for. It's an AC of France's Midi (deep south) and produces countless robust reds and a few interesting whites, often at bargain prices.

Cortese – White grape variety of Piedmont, Italy. At its best, makes amazingly delicious, keenly brisk and fascinating wines, including those of the Gavi DOCG. Worth seeking out.

Costières de Nîmes – Until 1989, this AC of southern France was known as the Costières de Gard. It forms a buffer between the southern Rhône

WHAT WINE WORDS MEAN

and Languedoc-Roussillon regions, and makes wines from broadly the same range of grape varieties. It's a name to look out for, the best red wines being notable for their concentration of colour and fruit, with the earthy-spiciness of the better Rhône wines and a likeable liquorice note. A few good white wines, too, and even a decent rosé or two.

Côte – In French, it simply means a side, or slope, of a hill. The implication in wine terms is that the grapes come from a vineyard ideally situated for maximum sunlight, good drainage and the unique soil conditions prevailing on the hill in question. It's fair enough to claim that vines grown on slopes might get more sunlight than those grown on the flat, but there is no guarantee whatsoever that any wine labelled 'Côtes du' this or that is made from grapes grown on a hillside anyway. Côtes du Rhône wines are a case in point. Many 'Côtes' wines come from entirely level vineyards and it is worth remembering that many of the vineyards of Bordeaux, producing most of the world's priciest wines, are little short of prairie-flat. The quality factor is determined much more significantly by the weather and the talents of the winemaker.

Coteaux Bourguignons – Generic AC of Burgundy, France, since 2011 for red and rosé wines from Pinot Noir and Gamay grapes, and white wines from (principally) Chardonnay and Bourgogne Aligoté grapes. The AC replaces the former appellation Bourgogne Grand Ordinaire.

Côtes de Blaye – Appellation Contrôlée zone of Bordeaux on the right bank of the River Gironde, opposite the more prestigious Médoc zone of the left bank. Best-rated vineyards qualify for the AC Premières Côtes de Blaye. A couple of centuries ago, Blaye (pronounced 'bligh') was the grander of the two, and even today makes some wines that compete well for quality, and at a fraction of the price of wines from its more fashionable rival across the water.

Côtes de Bourg – AC neighbouring Côtes de Blaye, making red wines of fast-improving quality and value.

Côtes du Luberon – Appellation Contrôlée zone of Provence in south-east France. Wines, mostly red, are similar in style to Côtes du Rhône.

Côtes du Rhône – One of the biggest and best-known appellations of south-east France, covering an area roughly defined by the southern reaches of the valley of the River Rhône. Long notorious for cheap and execrable reds, the Côtes du Rhône AC has lately achieved remarkable improvements in quality at all points along the price scale. Lots of brilliant-value warm and spicy reds, principally from Grenache and Syrah grapes. There are also some white and rosé wines.

Côtes du Rhône Villages – Appellation within the larger Côtes du Rhône AC for wine of supposed superiority made in a number of zones associated with a long list of nominated individual villages.

Côtes du Roussillon – Huge appellation of south-west France known for strong, dark, peppery reds often offering very decent value.

Côtes du Roussillon Villages – Appellation for superior wines from a number of nominated locations within the larger Roussillon AC. Some of these village wines can be of exceptional quality and value.

crianza – Means 'nursery' in Spanish. On Rioja and Navarra wines, the designation signifies a wine that has been nursed through a maturing period of at least a year in oak casks and a further six months in bottle before being released for sale.

cru – A word that crops up with confusing regularity on French wine labels. It means 'the growing' or 'the making' of a wine and asserts that the wine concerned is from a specific vineyard. Under the Appellation Contrôlée rules, countless *crus* are classified in various hierarchical ranks. Hundreds of individual vineyards are described as *premier cru* or *grand cru* in the classic wine regions of Alsace, Bordeaux, Burgundy and Champagne. The common denominator is that the wine can be counted on to be enormously expensive. On humbler wines, the use of the word *cru* tends to be mere decoration.

cru classé – *See* classed growth.

cuve – A vat for wine. French.

cuvée – French for the wine in a *cuve*, or vat. The word is much used on labels to imply that the wine is from just one vat, and thus of unique, unblended character. *Première cuvée* is supposedly the best wine from a given pressing because it comes from the free-run juice of grapes crushed by their own weight before pressing begins. Subsequent *cuvées* will have been from harsher pressings, grinding the grape pulp to extract the last drop of juice.

D

Dão – Major wine-producing region of northern Portugal now turning out much more interesting reds than it used to – worth looking out for anything made by mega-producer Sogrape.

demi sec – 'Half-dry' style of French (and some other) wines. Beware. It can mean anything from off-dry to cloyingly sweet.

DO – Denominación de Origen, Spain's wine-regulating scheme, similar to France's AC, but older – the first DO region was Rioja, from 1926. DO wines are Spain's best, accounting for a third of the nation's annual production.

DOC – Stands for Denominazione di Origine Controllata, Italy's equivalent of France's AC. The wines are made according to the stipulations of each of the system's 300-plus denominated zones of origin, along with a further 73 zones, which enjoy the superior classification of DOCG (DOC with *e Garantita* – guaranteed – appended).

DOCa – *Denominación de Origen Calificada* is Spain's highest regional wine classification; currently only Priorat and Rioja qualify.

DOP – Denominazione di Origine Protetta is an alternative classification to DOC (*qv*) under EU directive in Italy, comparable to AOP (*qv*) in France, but not yet widely adopted.

Durif – Rare black grape variety mostly of California, where it is also known as Petite Sirah, with some plantings in Australia.

E

earthy – A tricky word in the wine vocabulary. In this book, its use is meant to be complimentary. It indicates that the wine somehow suggests the soil the grapes were grown in, even (perhaps a shade too poetically) the landscape in which the vineyards lie. The amazing-value red wines of the torrid, volcanic southernmost regions of Italy are often described as earthy. This is an association with the pleasantly 'scorched' back-flavour in wines made from the ultra-ripe harvests of this near-sub-tropical part of the world.

edge – A wine with edge is one with evident (although not excessive) acidity.

élevé – 'Brought up' in French. Much used on wine labels where the wine has been matured (brought up) in oak barrels, *élevé en fûts de chêne*, to give it extra dimensions.

Entre Deux Mers – Meaning 'between two seas', it's a region lying between the Dordogne and Garonne rivers of Bordeaux, now mainly known for dry white wines from Sauvignon and Semillon grapes.

Estremadura – Wine-producing region occupying Portugal's coastal area north of Lisbon. Lots of interesting wines from indigenous grape varieties, usually at bargain prices. If a label mentions Estremadura, it is a safe rule that there might be something good within.

Extremadura – Minor wine-producing region of western Spain abutting the frontier with Portugal's Alentejo region. Not to be confused with Estremadura of Portugal (above).

F

Falanghina – Revived ancient grape variety of southern Italy now making some superbly fresh and tangy white wines.

Faugères – AC of the Languedoc in south-west France. Source of many hearty, economic reds.

Feteasca – White grape variety widely grown in Romania. Name means 'maiden's grape' and the wine tends to be soft and slightly sweet.

Fiano – White grape variety of the Campania of southern Italy and Sicily, lately revived. It is said to have been cultivated by the ancient Romans for a wine called Apianum.

finish – The last flavour lingering in the mouth after wine has been swallowed.

fino – Pale and very dry style of sherry. You drink it thoroughly chilled – and you don't keep it any longer after opening than other dry white wines. Needs to be fresh to be at its best.

Fitou – AC of Languedoc, France. Red wines principally from Carignan, Grenache, Mourvèdre and Syrah grapes.

flabby – Fun word describing a wine that tastes dilute or watery, with insufficient acidity.

Frappato – Black grape variety of Sicily. Light red wines.

fruit – In tasting terms, the fruit is the greater part of the overall flavour of a wine. The wine is (or should be) after all, composed entirely of fruit.

G

Gamay – The black grape that makes all red Beaujolais and some ordinary burgundy. It is a pretty safe rule to avoid Gamay wines from any other region, but there are exceptions.

Garganega – White grape variety of the Veneto region of north-east Italy. Best known as the principal ingredient of Soave, but occasionally included in varietal blends and mentioned as such on labels. Correctly pronounced 'gar-GAN-iga'.

Garnacha – Spanish black grape variety synonymous with Grenache of France. It is blended with Tempranillo to make the red wines of Rioja and Navarra, and is now quite widely cultivated elsewhere in Spain to make grippingly fruity varietals.

garrigue – Arid land of France's deep south giving its name to a style of red wine that notionally evokes the herby, heated, peppery flavours associated with such a landscape. A tricky metaphor!

Gavi – DOCG for dry but rich white wine from Cortese grapes in Piedmont, north-west Italy. Trendy Gavi di Gavi wines tend to be enjoyably lush, but are rather expensive.

Gewürztraminer – One of the great grape varieties of Alsace, France. At their best, the wines are perfumed with lychees and are richly, spicily fruity, yet quite dry. Gewürztraminer from Alsace can be expensive, but the grape is also grown with some success in Germany, Italy, New Zealand and South America, at more approachable prices. Pronounced 'ge-VOORTS-traminner'.

Givry – AC for red and white wines in the Côte Chalonnaise sub-region of Burgundy. Source of some wonderfully natural-tasting reds that might be lighter than those of the more prestigious Côte d'Or to the north, but have great merits of their own. Relatively, the wines are often underpriced.

Glera – Alternative name for Prosecco grape of northern Italy.

Godello – White grape variety of Galicia, Spain.

Graciano – Black grape variety of Spain that is one of the minor constituents of Rioja. Better known in its own right in Australia where it can make dense, spicy, long-lived red wines.

green – I don't often use this in the pejorative. Green, to me, is a likeable degree of freshness, especially in Sauvignon Blanc wines.

Grecanico – White grape variety of southern Italy, especially Sicily. Aromatic, grassy dry white wines.

Greco – White grape variety of southern Italy believed to be of ancient Greek origin. Big-flavoured dry white wines.

Grenache – The mainstay of the wines of the southern Rhône Valley in France. Grenache is usually the greater part of the mix in Côtes du Rhône reds and is widely planted right across the neighbouring Languedoc-Roussillon region. It's a big-cropping variety that thrives even in the hottest climates and is really a blending grape – most commonly with Syrah, the noble variety of the northern Rhône. Few French wines are labelled with its name, but the grape has caught on in Australia in a big way and it is now becoming a familiar varietal, known for strong, dark liquorous reds. Grenache is the French name for what is originally a Spanish variety, Garnacha.

Grillo – White grape of Sicily said to be among the island's oldest indigenous varieties, pre-dating the arrival of the Greeks in 600 BC. Much used for fortified Marsala, it has lately been revived for interesting, aromatic dry table wines.

grip – In wine-tasting terminology, the sensation in the mouth produced by a wine that has a healthy quantity of tannin in it. A wine with grip is a good wine. A wine with too much tannin, or which is still too young (the tannin hasn't 'softened' with age) is not described as having grip, but as mouth-puckering – or simply undrinkable.

Grolleau – Black grape variety of the Loire Valley principally cultivated for Rosé d'Anjou.

Gros Plant – White grape variety of the Pays Nantais in France's Loire estuary; synonymous with the Folle Blanche grape of south-west France.

Grüner Veltliner – The 'national' white-wine grape of Austria. In the past it made mostly soft, German-style everyday wines, but now is behind some excellent dry styles, too.

H

halbtrocken – 'Half-dry' in Germany's wine vocabulary. A reassurance that the wine is not some ghastly sugared Liebfraumilch-style confection.

hard – In red wine, a flavour denoting excess tannin, probably due to immaturity.

Haut-Médoc – Extensive AOC of Bordeaux accounting for the greater part of the vineyard area to the north of the city of Bordeaux and west of the Gironde river. The Haut-Médoc incorporates the prestigious commune-AOCs of Listrac, Margaux, Moulis, Pauillac, St Estephe and St Julien.

hock – The wine of Germany's Rhine river valleys. Traditionally, but no longer consistently, it comes in brown bottles, as distinct from the wine of the Mosel river valleys – which comes in green ones.

I

Indicación Geográfica Protegida – Spain's country-wine quality designation covers 46 zones across the country. Wines made under the IGP can be labelled Vino de la Tierra.

Indication Géographique Protégée (IGP) – Introduced to France in 2010 under EU-wide wine-designation rules, IGP covers the wines previously known as vins de pays. Some wines are currently labelled IGP, but established vins de pays producers are redesignating slowly, if at all, and are not obliged to do so. Some will abbreviate, so, for example, Vin de Pays d'Oc shortens to Pays d'Oc.

Indicazione Geografica Tipica – Italian wine-quality designation, broadly equivalent to France's IGP. The label has to state the geographical location of the vineyard and will often (but not always) state the principal grape varieties from which the wine is made.

isinglass – A gelatinous material used in fining (clarifying) wine. It is derived from fish bladders and consequently is eschewed by makers of 'vegetarian' wines.

J

jammy – The 'sweetness' in dry red wines is supposed to evoke ripeness rather than sugariness. Sometimes, flavours include a sweetness reminiscent of jam. Usually a fault in the winemaking technique.

Jerez – Wine town of Andalucia, Spain, and home to sherry. The English word 'sherry' is a simple mispronunciation of Jerez.

joven – Young wine, Spanish. In regions such as Rioja, *vino joven* is a synonym for *sin crianza*, which means 'without ageing' in cask or bottle.

Jura – Wine region of eastern France incorporating four AOCs, Arbois, Château-Chalon, Côtes du Jura and L'Etoile. Known for still red, white and rosé wines and sparkling wines as well as exotic *vin de paille* and *vin jaune*.

Jurançon – Appellation for white wines from Courbu and Manseng grapes at Pau, south-west France.

K

Kabinett – Under Germany's bewildering wine-quality rules, this is a classification of a top-quality (QmP) wine. Expect a keen, dry, racy style. The name comes from the cabinet or cupboard in which winemakers traditionally kept their most treasured bottles.

Kekfrankos – Black grape variety of Hungary, particularly the Sopron region, which makes some of the country's more interesting red wines, characterised by colour and spiciness. Same variety as Austria's Blaufrankisch.

L

Ladoix – Unfashionable AC at northern edge of Côtes de Beaune makes some of Burgundy's true bargain reds. A name to look out for.

Lambrusco – The name is that of a black grape variety widely grown across northern Italy. True Lambrusco wine is red, dry and very slightly sparkling, but from the 1980s Britain was deluged with a strange, sweet manifestation of the style, which has done little to enhance the good name of the original. Good Lambrusco is delicious and fun, and now enjoying a welcome revival in Britain.

Languedoc-Roussillon – Wine guaranteed to have been produced in France. The source, now, of many great-value wines from countless ACs and vin de pays zones.

lees – The detritus of the winemaking process that collects in the bottom of the vat or cask. Wines left for extended periods on the lees can acquire extra dimensions of flavour, in particular a 'leesy' creaminess.

legs – The liquid residue left clinging to the sides of the glass after wine has been swirled. The persistence of the legs is an indicator of the weight of alcohol. Also known as 'tears'.

lieu dit – This is starting to appear on French wine labels. It translates as an 'agreed place' and is an area of vineyard defined as of particular character or merit, but not classified under wine law. Usually, the *lieu dit*'s name is stated, with the implication that the wine in question has special value.

liquorice – The pungent, slightly burnt flavours of this once-fashionable confection are detectable in some wines made from very ripe grapes, for example, the Malbec harvested in Argentina and several varieties grown in the very hot vineyards of southernmost Italy. A close synonym is 'tarry'. This characteristic is by no means a fault in red wine, unless very dominant, but it can make for a challenging flavour that might not appeal to all tastes.

liquorous – Wines of great weight and glyceriney texture (evidenced by the 'legs', or 'tears', which cling to the glass after the wine has been swirled) are always noteworthy. The connection with liquor is drawn in respect of the feel of the wine in the mouth, rather than with the higher alcoholic strength of spirits.

Lirac – Village and AOC of southern Rhône Valley, France. A near-neighbour of the esteemed appellation of Châteauneuf du Pape, Lirac makes red wine of comparable depth and complexity, at competitive prices.

Lugana – DOC of Lombardy, Italy, known for a dry white wine that is often of real distinction – rich, almondy stuff from the ubiquitous Trebbiano grape.

M

Macabeo – One of the main grapes used for cava, the sparkling wine of Spain. It is the same grape as Viura.

Mâcon – Town and collective appellation of southern Burgundy, France. Lightweight white wines from Chardonnay grapes and similarly light reds from Pinot Noir and some Gamay. The better ones, and the ones exported, have the AC Mâcon-Villages and there are individual village wines with their own ACs including Mâcon-Clessé, Mâcon-Viré and Mâcon-Lugny.

Malbec – Black grape variety grown on a small scale in Bordeaux, and the mainstay of the wines of Cahors in France's Dordogne region under the name Cot. Now much better known for producing big butch reds in Argentina.

manzanilla – Pale, very dry sherry of Sanlucar de Barrameda, a resort town on the Bay of Cadiz in Spain. Manzanilla is proud to be distinct from the pale, very dry fino sherry of the main producing town of Jerez de la Frontera an hour's drive inland. Drink it chilled and fresh – it goes downhill in an opened bottle after just a few days, even if kept (as it should be) in the fridge.

Margaret River – Vineyard region of Western Australia regarded as ideal for grape varieties including Cabernet Sauvignon. It has a relatively cool climate and a reputation for making sophisticated wines, both red and white.

Marlborough – Best-known vineyard region of New Zealand's South Island has a cool climate and a name for brisk but cerebral Sauvignon Blanc and Chardonnay wines.

Marsanne – White grape variety of the northern Rhône Valley and, increasingly, of the wider south of France. It's known for making well-coloured wines with heady aroma and fruit.

Mataro – Black grape variety of Australia. It's the same as the Mourvèdre of France and Monastrell of Spain.

Mazuelo – Spanish name for France's black grape variety Carignan.

McLaren Vale – Vineyard region south of Adelaide in south-east Australia. Known for blockbuster Shiraz (and Chardonnay) that can be of great balance and quality from winemakers who keep the ripeness under control.

meaty – Weighty, rich red wine style.

Mencia – Black grape variety of Galicia and north-west Spain. Light red wines.

Mendoza – The region to watch in Argentina. Lying to the east of the Andes mountains, just about opposite the best vineyards of Chile on the other side, Mendoza accounts for the bulk of Argentine wine production, with quality improving fast.

Merlot – One of the great black wine grapes of Bordeaux, and now grown all over the world. The name is said to derive from the French *merle*, meaning a blackbird. Characteristics of Merlot-based wines attract descriptions such as 'plummy' and 'plump' with black-cherry aroma. The grapes are larger than most, and thus have less skin in proportion to their flesh. This means the resulting wines have less tannin than wines from smaller-berry varieties such as Cabernet Sauvignon, and are therefore, in the Bordeaux context at least, more suitable for drinking while still relatively young.

middle palate – In wine tasting, the impression given by the wine when it is held in the mouth.

Midi – Catch-all term for the deep south of France west of the Rhône Valley.

mineral – I am trying to excise this overused word from my notes, but not so far managing to do so with much conviction. To me it evokes flavours such as the stone-pure freshness of some Loire dry whites, or the steely quality of the more austere style of the Chardonnay grape, especially in Chablis. Mineral really just means something mined, as in dug out of the ground, like iron ore (as in steel) or rock, as in, er, stone. Maybe there's something in it, but I am not entirely confident.

Minervois – AC for (mostly) red wines from vineyards around the town of Minerve in the Languedoc-Roussillon region of France. Often good value. The new Minervois La Livinière AC – a sort of Minervois *grand cru* – is host to some great estates including Château Maris and Vignobles Lorgeril.

Monastrell – Black grape variety of Spain, widely planted in Mediterranean regions for inexpensive wines notable for their high alcohol and toughness – though they can mature into excellent, soft reds. The variety is known in France as Mourvèdre and in Australia as Mataro.

Monbazillac – AC for sweet, dessert wines within the wider appellation of Bergerac in south-west France. Made from the same grape varieties (principally Sauvignon and Semillon) that go into the much costlier counterpart wines of Barsac and Sauternes near Bordeaux, these stickies from botrytis-affected, late-harvested grapes can be delicious and good value for money.

Montalcino – Hill town of Tuscany, Italy, and a DOCG for strong and very long-lived red wines from Brunello grapes. The wines are mostly very expensive. Rosso di Montalcino, a DOC for the humbler wines of the zone, is often a good buy.

Montepulciano – Black grape variety of Italy. Best known in Montepulciano d'Abruzzo, the juicy, purply-black and bramble-fruited red of the Abruzzi region midway down Italy's Adriatic side. Also the grape in the rightly popular hearty reds of Rosso Conero from around Ancona in the Marches. Not to be confused with the hill town of Montepulciano in Tuscany, famous for expensive Vino Nobile di Montepulciano wine.

morello – Lots of red wines have smells and flavours redolent of cherries. Morello cherries, among the darkest coloured and sweetest of all varieties and the preferred choice of cherry-brandy producers, have a distinct sweetness resembled by some wines made from Merlot grapes. A morello whiff or taste is generally very welcome.

Moscatel – Spanish Muscat.

Moscato – *See* Muscat.

Moselle – The wine of Germany's Mosel river valleys, collectively known for winemaking purposes as Mosel-Saar-Ruwer. The wine always comes in slim, green bottles, as distinct from the brown bottles traditionally, but no longer exclusively, employed for Rhine wines.

Mourvèdre – Widely planted black grape variety of southern France. It's an ingredient in many of the wines of Provence, the Rhône and Languedoc, including the ubiquitous Vin de Pays d'Oc. It's a hot-climate vine and the wine is usually blended with other varieties to give sweet aromas and 'backbone' to the mix. Known as Mataro in Australia and Monastrell in Spain.

Muscadet – One of France's most familiar everyday whites, made from a grape called the Melon or Melon de Bourgogne. It comes from vineyards at the estuarial end of the River Loire, and has a sea-breezy freshness about it. The better wines are reckoned to be those from the vineyards in the Sèvre et Maine region, and many are made *sur lie* – 'on the lees' – meaning that the wine is left in contact with the yeasty deposit of its fermentation until just before bottling, in an endeavour to add interest to what can sometimes be an acidic and fruitless style.

Muscat – Grape variety with origins in ancient Greece, and still grown widely among the Aegean islands for the production of sweet white wines. Muscats are the wines that taste more like grape juice than any other – but the high sugar levels ensure they are also among the most alcoholic of wines, too. Known as Moscato in Italy, the grape is much used for making sweet sparkling wines, as in Asti Spumante or Moscato d'Asti. There are several appellations in south-west France for inexpensive Muscats made rather like port, part-fermented before the addition of grape alcohol to halt the conversion of sugar into alcohol, creating a sweet and heady *vin doux naturel*. Dry Muscat wines, when well made, have a delicious sweet aroma but a refreshing, light touch with flavours reminiscent variously of orange blossom, wood smoke and grapefruit.

must – New-pressed grape juice prior to fermentation.

N

Navarra – DO wine-producing region of northern Spain adjacent to, and overshadowed by, Rioja. Navarra's wines can be startlingly akin to their neighbouring rivals, and sometimes rather better value for money.

négociant – In France, a dealer-producer who buys wines from growers and matures and/or blends them for sale under his or her own label. Purists can be a bit sniffy about these entrepreneurs, claiming that only the vine-grower with his or her own winemaking set-up can make truly authentic stuff, but the truth is that many of the best wines of France are *négociant*-produced – especially at the humbler end of the price scale. *Négociants* are often identified on wine labels as *négociant-éleveur* (literally 'dealer-bringer-up'), meaning that the wine has been matured, blended and bottled by the party in question.

Negroamaro – Black grape variety mainly of Puglia, the much-lauded wine region of south-east Italy. Dense, earthy red wines with ageing potential and plenty of alcohol. The grape behind Copertino, Salice Salentio and Squinzano.

Nerello Mascalese – Black grape of Sicily making light, flavoursome and alcoholic reds.

Nero d'Avola – Black grape variety of Sicily and southern Italy. It makes deep-coloured wines that, given half a chance, can develop intensity and richness with age.

non-vintage – A wine is described as such when it has been blended from the harvests of more than one year. A non-vintage wine is not necessarily an inferior one, but under quality-control regulations around the world, still table wines most usually derive solely from one year's grape crop to qualify for appellation status. Champagnes and sparkling wines are mostly blended from several vintages, as are fortified wines, such as basic port and sherry.

nose – In the vocabulary of the wine-taster, the nose is the scent of a wine. Sounds a bit dotty, but it makes a sensible enough alternative to the rather bald 'smell'. The use of the word 'perfume' implies that the wine smells particularly good. 'Aroma' is used specifically to describe a wine that smells as it should, as in 'this burgundy has the authentic strawberry-raspberry aroma of Pinot Noir'.

O

oak – Most of the world's costliest wines are matured in new or nearly new oak barrels, giving additional opulence of flavour. Of late, many cheaper wines have been getting the oak treatment, too, in older, cheaper casks, or simply by having sacks of oak chippings poured into their steel or fibreglass holding tanks. 'Oak aged' on a label is likely to indicate the latter treatments. But the overtly oaked wines of Australia have in some cases been so overdone that there is now a reactive trend whereby some producers proclaim their wines – particularly Chardonnays – as 'unoaked' on the label, thereby asserting that the flavours are more naturally achieved.

Oltrepo Pavese – Wine-producing zone of Piedmont, north-west Italy. The name means 'south of Pavia across the [river] Po' and the wines, both white and red, can be excellent quality and value for money.

organic wine – As in other sectors of the food industry, demand for organically made wine is – or appears to be – growing. As a rule, a wine qualifies as organic if it comes entirely from grapes grown in vineyards cultivated without the use of synthetic materials, and made in a winery where chemical treatments or additives are shunned with similar vigour. In fact, there are plenty of winemakers in the world using organic methods, but who disdain to label their bottles as such. Wines proclaiming their organic status used to carry the same sort of premium as their counterparts round the corner in the fruit, vegetable and meat aisles. But organic viticulture is now commonplace and there seems little price impact. There is no single worldwide (or even Europe-wide) standard for organic food or wine, so you pretty much have to take the producer's word for it.

P

Pasqua – One of the biggest and, it should be said, best wine producers of the Veneto region of north-west Italy.

Passetoutgrains – Bourgogne Passetoutgrains is a generic appellation of the Burgundy region, France. The word loosely means 'any grapes allowed' and is supposed specifically to designate a red wine made with Gamay grapes as well as Burgundy's principal black variety, Pinot Noir, in a ratio of two parts Gamay to one of Pinot. The wine is usually relatively inexpensive, and relatively uninteresting, too.

Pays d'Oc – Shortened form under recent rule changes of French wine designation Vin de Pays d'Oc. All other similar regional designations can be similarly abbreviated.

Pecorino – White grape variety of mid-eastern Italy currently in vogue for well-coloured dry white varietal wines.

Periquita – Black grape variety of southern Portugal. Makes rather exotic spicy reds. Name means 'parrot'.

Perricone – Black grape variety of Sicily. Low-acid red wines.

PET – It's what they call plastic wine bottles – lighter to transport and allegedly as ecological as glass. Polyethylene terephthalate.

Petit Verdot – Black grape variety of Bordeaux used to give additional colour, density and spiciness to Cabernet Sauvignon-dominated blends. Mostly a minority player at home, but in Australia and California it is grown as the principal variety for some big hearty reds of real character.

petrol – When white wines from certain grapes, especially Riesling, are allowed to age in the bottle for longer than a year or two, they can take on a spiry aroma reminiscent of petrol or diesel. In grand mature German wines, this is considered a very good thing.

Picpoul – Grape variety of southern France. Best known in Picpoul de Pinet, a dry white from near Carcassonne in the Languedoc, newly elevated to AOP status. The name Picpoul (also Piquepoul) means 'stings the lips' – referring to the natural high acidity of the juice.

Piemonte – North-western province of Italy, which we call Piedmont, known for the spumante wines of the town of Asti, plus expensive Barbaresco and Barolo and better-value varietal red wines from Barbera and Dolcetto grapes.

Pinotage – South Africa's own black grape variety. Makes red wines ranging from light and juicy to dark, strong and long-lived. It's a cross between Pinot Noir and a grape the South Africans used to call Hermitage (thus the portmanteau name) but turns out to have been Cinsault.

Pinot Blanc – White grape variety principally of Alsace, France. Florally perfumed, exotically fruity dry white wines.

Pinot Grigio – White grape variety of northern Italy. Wines bearing its name are perplexingly fashionable. Good examples have an interesting smoky-pungent aroma and keen, slaking fruit. But most are dull. Originally French, it is at its best in the lushly exotic Pinot Gris wines of Alsace and is also successfully cultivated in Germany and New Zealand.

Pinot Noir – The great black grape of Burgundy, France. It makes all the region's fabulously expensive red wines. Notoriously difficult to grow in warmer climates, it is nevertheless cultivated by countless intrepid winemakers in the New World intent on reproducing the magic appeal of red burgundy. California and New Zealand have come closest, but rarely at prices much below those for the real thing. Some Chilean Pinot Noirs are inexpensive and worth trying.

Pouilly Fuissé – Village and AC of the Mâconnais region of southern Burgundy in France. Dry white wines from Chardonnay grapes. Wines are among the highest rated of the Mâconnais.

Pouilly Fumé – Village and AC of the Loire Valley in France. Dry white wines from Sauvignon Blanc grapes. Similar 'pebbly', 'grassy' or even 'gooseberry' style to neighbouring AC Sancerre. The notion put about by some enthusiasts that Pouilly Fumé is 'smoky' is surely nothing more than word association with the name.

Primitivo – Black grape variety of southern Italy, especially the region of Puglia. Named from Latin *primus* for first, the grape is among the earliest-ripening of all varieties. The wines are typically dense and dark in colour with plenty of alcohol, and have an earthy, spicy style. Often a real bargain.

Priorat – Emerging wine region of Catalonia, Spain. Highly valued red wines from Garnacha and other varieties.

Prosecco – White grape variety of Italy's Veneto region known entirely for the softly sparkling wine it makes. The best come from the DOCG Conegliano-Valdobbiadene, made as spumante ('foaming') wines in pressurised tanks, typically to 11 per cent alcohol and ranging from softly sweet to crisply dry. Now trendy, but the cheap wines – one leading brand comes in a can – are of very variable quality.

Puglia – The region occupying the 'heel' of southern Italy, lately making many good, inexpensive wines from indigenous grape varieties.

Q

QbA – German, standing for Qualitätswein bestimmter Anbaugebiete. It means 'quality wine from designated areas' and implies that the wine is made from grapes with a minimum level of ripeness, but it's by no means a guarantee of exciting quality. Only wines labelled QmP (see next entry) can be depended upon to be special.

QmP – Stands for Qualitätswein mit Prädikat. These are the serious wines of Germany, made without the addition of sugar to 'improve' them. To qualify for QmP status, the grapes must reach a level of ripeness as measured on a sweetness scale – all according to Germany's fiendishly complicated wine-quality regulations. Wines from grapes that reach the stated minimum level of sweetness qualify for the description of Kabinett. The next level up earns the rank of Spätlese, meaning 'late-picked'. Kabinett wines can be expected to be dry and brisk in style, and Spätlese wines a little bit riper and fuller. The next grade up, Auslese, meaning 'selected harvest', indicates a wine made from super-ripe grapes; it will be golden in colour and honeyed in flavour. A generation ago, these wines were as valued, and as expensive, as any of the world's grandest appellations.

Quincy – AC of Loire Valley, France, known for pebbly-dry white wines from Sauvignon grapes. The wines are forever compared to those of nearby and much better-known Sancerre – and Quincy often represents better value for money. Pronounced 'KAN-see'.

Quinta – Portuguese for farm or estate. It precedes the names of many of Portugal's best-known wines. It is pronounced 'KEEN-ta'.

R

racy – Evocative wine-tasting description for wine that thrills the tastebuds with a rush of exciting sensations. Good Rieslings often qualify.

raisiny – Wines from grapes that have been very ripe or overripe at harvest can take on a smell and flavour akin to the concentrated, heat-dried sweetness of raisins. As a minor element in the character of a wine, this can add to the appeal but as a dominant characteristic it is a fault.

rancio – Spanish term harking back to Roman times when wines were commonly stored in jars outside, exposed to the sun, so they oxidised and took on a burnt sort of flavour. Today, *rancio* describes a baked – and by no means unpleasant – flavour in fortified wines, particularly sherry and Madeira.

Reserva – In Portugal and Spain, this has genuine significance. The Portuguese use it for special wines with a higher alcohol level and longer ageing, although the precise periods vary between regions. In Spain, especially in the Navarra and Rioja regions, it means the wine must have had at least a year in oak and two in bottle before release.

reserve – On French (as *réserve*) or other wines, this implies special-quality, longer-aged wines, but has no official significance.

Retsina – The universal white wine of Greece. It has been traditionally made in Attica, the region of Athens, for a very long time, and is said to owe its origins and name to the ancient custom of sealing amphorae (terracotta jars) of the wine with a gum made from pine resin. Some of the flavour of the resin inevitably transmitted itself into the wine, and ancient Greeks acquired a lasting taste for it.

Reuilly – AC of Loire Valley, France, for crisp dry whites from Sauvignon grapes. Pronounced 'RER-yee'.

Ribatejo – Emerging wine region of Portugal. Worth seeking out on labels of red wines in particular, because new winemakers are producing lively stuff from distinctive indigenous grapes such as Castelao and Trincadeira.

Ribera del Duero – Classic wine region of north-west Spain lying along the River Duero (which crosses the border to become Portugal's Douro, forming the valley where port comes from). It is home to an estate rather oddly named Vega Sicilia, where red wines of epic quality are made and sold at equally epic prices. Further down the scale, some very good reds are made, too.

Riesling – The noble grape variety of Germany. It is correctly pronounced 'REEZ-ling', not 'RICE-ling'. Once notorious as the grape behind all those boring 'medium' Liebfraumilches and Niersteiners, this grape has had a bad press. In fact, there has never been much, if ány, Riesling in Germany's cheap-and-nasty plonks. But the country's best wines, the so-called Qualitätswein mit Prädikat grades, are made almost exclusively with Riesling. These wines range from crisply fresh and appley styles to extravagantly fruity, honeyed wines from late-harvested grapes. Excellent Riesling wines are also made in Alsace and now in Australia.

Rioja – The principal fine-wine region of Spain, in the country's north east. The pricier wines are noted for their vanilla-pod richness from long ageing in oak casks. Tempranillo and Garnacha grapes make the reds, Viura the whites.

Ripasso – A particular style of Valpolicella wine. New wine is partially refermented in vats that have been used to make the Recioto reds (wines made from semi-dried grapes), thus creating a bigger, smoother version of usually light and pale Valpolicella.

Riserva – In Italy, a wine made only in the best vintages, and allowed longer ageing in cask and bottle.

Rivaner – Alternative name for Germany's Müller-Thurgau grape, the life-blood of Liebfraumilch.

Riverland – Vineyard region to the immediate north of the Barossa Valley of South Australia, extending east into New South Wales.

Roditis – White grape variety of Greece, known for fresh dry whites with decent acidity, often included in retsina.

rosso – Red wine, Italy.

Rosso Conero – DOC red wine made in the environs of Ancona in the Marches, Italy. Made from the Montepulciano grape, the wine can provide excellent value for money.

Ruby Cabernet – Black grape variety of California, created by crossing Cabernet Sauvignon and Carignan. Makes soft and squelchy red wine at home and in South Africa.

Rueda – DO of north-west Spain making first-class refreshing dry whites from the indigenous Verdejo grape, imported Sauvignon, and others. Exciting quality, and prices are keen.

Rully – AC of Chalonnais region of southern Burgundy, France. White wines from Chardonnay and red wines from Pinot Noir grapes. Both can be very good and are substantially cheaper than their more northerly Burgundian neighbours. Pronounced 'ROO-yee'.

S

Saint Emilion – AC of Bordeaux, France. Centred on the romantic hill town of St Emilion, this famous sub-region makes some of the grandest red wines of France, but also some of the best-value ones. Less fashionable than the Médoc region on the opposite (west) bank of the River Gironde that bisects Bordeaux, St Emilion wines are made largely with the Merlot grape, and are relatively quick to mature. The top wines are classified *1er grand cru classé* and are madly expensive, but many more are classified respectively *grand cru classé* and *grand cru*, and these designations can be seen as a fairly trustworthy indicator of quality. There are several 'satellite' St Emilion ACs named after the villages at their centres, notably Lussac St Emilion, Montagne St Emilion and Puisseguin St Emilion. Some excellent wines are made by estates within these ACs, and at relatively affordable prices thanks to the comparatively humble status of their satellite designations.

Salento – Up-and-coming wine region of southern Italy. Many good bargain reds from local grapes including Nero d'Avola and Primitivo.

Sancerre – AC of the Loire Valley, France, renowned for flinty-fresh Sauvignon whites and rarer Pinot Noir reds. These wines are never cheap, and recent tastings make it plain that only the best-made, individual-producer wines are worth the money. Budget brands seem mostly dull.

Sangiovese – The local black grape of Tuscany, Italy. It is the principal variety used for Chianti and is now widely planted in Latin America – often making delicious, Chianti-like wines with characteristic cherryish-but-deeply-ripe fruit and a dry, clean finish. Chianti wines have become (unjustifiably) expensive in recent years and cheaper Italian wines such as those called Sangiovese di Toscana make a consoling substitute.

Saumur – Town and appellation of Loire Valley, France. Characterful minerally red wines from Cabernet Franc grapes, and some whites. The once-popular sparkling wines from Chenin Blanc grapes are now little seen in Britain.

Saumur-Champigny – Separate appellation for red wines from Cabernet Franc grapes of Saumur in the Loire, sometimes very good and lively.

Sauvignon Blanc – French white grape variety now grown worldwide. New Zealand is successfully challenging the long supremacy of French ACs such as Sancerre. The wines are characterised by aromas of gooseberry, fresh-cut grass, even asparagus. Flavours are often described as 'grassy' or 'nettly'.

sec – Dry wine style. French.

secco – Dry wine style. Italian.

Semillon – White grape variety originally of Bordeaux, where it is blended with Sauvignon Blanc to make fresh dry whites and, when harvested very late in the season, the ambrosial sweet whites of Barsac, Sauternes and other appellations. Even in the driest wines, the grape can be recognised from its honeyed, sweet-pineapple, even banana-like aromas. Now widely planted in Australia and Latin America, and frequently blended with Chardonnay to make dry whites, some of them interesting.

sherry – The great aperitif wine of Spain, centred on the Andalusian city of Jerez (from which the name 'sherry' is an English mispronunciation). There is a lot of sherry-style wine in the world, but only the authentic wine from Jerez and the neighbouring producing towns of Puerta de Santa Maria and Sanlucar de Barrameda may label their wines as such. The Spanish drink real sherry – very dry and fresh, pale in colour and served well-chilled – called fino and manzanilla, and darker but naturally dry variations called amontillado, palo cortado and oloroso.

Shiraz – Australian name for the Syrah grape. The variety is the most widely planted of any in Australia, and makes red wines of wildly varying quality, characterised by dense colour, high alcohol, spicy fruit and generous, cushiony texture.

Somontano – Wine region of north-east Spain. Name means 'under the mountains' – in this case the Pyrenees – and the region has had DO status since 1984. Much innovative winemaking here, with New World styles emerging. Some very good buys. A region to watch.

souple – French wine-tasting term that translates into English as 'supple' or even 'docile' as in 'pliable', but I understand it in the vinous context to mean muscular but soft – a wine with tannin as well as soft fruit.

Spätlese – *See* QmP.

spirity – Some wines, mostly from the New World, are made from grapes so ripe at harvest that their high alcohol content can be detected through a mildly burning sensation on the tongue, similar to the effect of sipping a spirit.

spritzy – Describes a wine with a barely detectable sparkle. Some young wines are intended to have this elusive fizziness; in others it is a fault.

spumante – Sparkling wine of Italy. Asti Spumante is the best known, from the town of Asti in the north-west Italian province of Piemonte. The term describes wines that are fully sparkling. Frizzante wines have a less vigorous mousse.

stalky – A useful tasting term to describe red wines with flavours that make you think the stalks from the grape bunches must have been fermented along with the must (juice). Young Bordeaux reds very often have this mild astringency. In moderation it's fine, but if it dominates it probably signifies the wine is at best immature and at worst badly made.

Stellenbosch – Town and region at the heart of South Africa's burgeoning wine industry. It's an hour's drive from Cape Town and the source of much of the country's cheaper wine. Quality is variable, and the name Stellenbosch on a label can't (yet, anyway) be taken as a guarantee of quality.

stony – Wine-tasting term for keenly dry white wines. It's meant to indicate a wine of purity and real quality, with just the right match of fruit and acidity.

structured – Good wines are not one-dimensional, they have layers of flavour and texture. A structured wine has phases of enjoyment: the 'attack', or first impression in the mouth; the middle palate as the wine is held in the mouth; and the lingering aftertaste.

summer fruit – Wine-tasting term intended to convey a smell or taste of soft fruits such as strawberries and raspberries – without having to commit too specifically to which.

superiore – On labels of Italian wines, this is more than an idle boast. Under DOC rules, wines must qualify for the *superiore* designation by reaching one or more specified quality levels, usually a higher alcohol content or an additional period of maturation. Frascati, for example, qualifies for DOC status at 11.5 per cent alcohol, but to be classified *superiore* must have 12 per cent alcohol.

sur lie – Literally, 'on the lees'. It's a term now widely used on the labels of Muscadet wines, signifying that after fermentation has died down, the new wine has been left in the tank over the winter on the lees – the detritus of yeasts and other interesting compounds left over from the turbid fermentation process. The idea is that additional interest is imparted into the flavour of the wine.

Syrah – The noble grape of the Rhône Valley, France. Makes very dark, dense wine characterised by peppery, tarry aromas. Now planted all over southern France and farther afield. In Australia, where it makes wines ranging from disagreeably jam-like plonks to wonderfully rich and silky keeping wines, it is known as Shiraz.

T

table wine – Wine that is unfortified and of an alcoholic strength, for UK tax purposes anyway, of no more than 15 per cent. I use the term to distinguish, for example, between the red table wines of the Douro Valley in Portugal and the region's better-known fortified wine, port.

Tafelwein – Table wine, German. The humblest quality designation, which doesn't usually bode very well.

tank method – Bulk-production process for sparkling wines. Base wine undergoes secondary fermentation in a large, sealed vat rather than in individual closed bottles. Also known as the Charmat method after the name of the inventor of the process.

Tai – White grape variety of north-east Italy, a relative of Sauvignon Blanc. Also known in Italy as Tocai Friulano or, more correctly, Friulano.

Tannat – Black grape of south-west France, notably for wines of Madiran, and lately named as the variety most beneficial to health thanks to its outstanding antioxidant content.

tannin – Well known as the film-forming, teeth-coating component in tea, tannin is a natural compound that occurs in black grape skins and acts as a natural preservative in wine. Its noticeable presence in wine is regarded as a good thing. It gives young everyday reds their dryness, firmness of flavour and backbone. And it helps high-quality reds to retain their lively fruitiness for many years. A grand Bordeaux red when first made, for example, will have purply-sweet, rich fruit and mouth-puckering tannin, but after ten years or so this will have evolved into a delectably fruity, mature wine in which the formerly parching effects of the tannin have receded almost completely, leaving the shade of 'residual tannin' that marks out a great wine approaching maturity.

Tarrango – Black grape variety of Australia.

tarry – On the whole, winemakers don't like critics to say their wines evoke the redolence of road repairs, but I can't help using this term to describe the agreeable, sweet, 'burnt' flavour that is often found at the centre of the fruit in wines from Argentina, Italy and Portugal in particular.

TCA – Dreaded ailment in wine, usually blamed on faulty corks. It stands for 246 *trichloroanisol* and is characterised by a horrible musty smell and flavour in the affected wine. It is largely because of the current plague of TCA that so many wine producers worldwide are now going over to polymer 'corks' and screwcaps.

tears – The colourless alcohol in the wine left clinging to the inside of the glass after the contents have been swirled. Persistent tears (also known as 'legs') indicate a wine of good concentration.

Tempranillo – The great black grape of Spain. Along with Garnacha (Grenache in France) it makes all red Rioja and Navarra wines and, under many pseudonyms, is an important or exclusive contributor to the wines of many other regions of Spain. It is also widely cultivated in South America.

Teroldego – Black grape variety of Trentino, northern Italy. Often known as Teroldego Rotaliano after the Rotaliano region where most of the vineyards lie. Deep-coloured, assertive, green-edged red wines.

tinto – On Spanish labels indicates a deeply coloured red wine. Clarete denotes a paler colour. Also Portuguese.

Toro – Quality wine region east of Zamora, Spain.

Torrontes – White grape variety of Argentina. Makes soft, dry wines often with delicious grapey-spicy aroma, similar in style to the classic dry Muscat wines of Alsace, but at more accessible prices.

Touraine – Region encompassing a swathe of the Loire Valley, France. Non-AC wines may be labelled 'Sauvignon de Touraine' etc.

Touriga Nacional – The most valued black grape variety of the Douro Valley in Portugal, where port is made. The name Touriga now appears on an increasing number of table wines made as sidelines by the port producers. They can be very good, with the same spirity aroma and sleek flavours of port itself, minus the fortification.

Traminer – Grape variety, the same as Gewürztraminer.

Trebbiano – The workhorse white grape of Italy. A productive variety that is easy to cultivate, it seems to be included in just about every ordinary white wine of the entire nation – including Frascati, Orvieto and Soave. It is the same grape as France's Ugni Blanc. There are, however, distinct regional variations of the grape. Trebbiano di Lugana makes a distinctive white in the DOC of the name, sometimes very good, while Trebbiano di

Toscana makes a major contribution to the distinctly less interesting dry whites of Chianti country.

Trincadeira Preta – Portuguese black grape variety native to the port-producing vineyards of the Douro Valley (where it goes under the name Tinta Amarella). In southern Portugal, it produces dark and sturdy table wines.

trocken – 'Dry' German wine. It's a recent trend among commercial-scale producers in the Rhine and Mosel to label their wines with this description in the hope of reassuring consumers that the contents do not resemble the dreaded sugar-water Liebfraumilch-type plonks of the bad old days. But the description does have a particular meaning under German wine law, namely that there is only a low level of unfermented sugar lingering in the wine (9 grams per litre, if you need to know), and this can leave the wine tasting rather austere.

U

Ugni Blanc – The most widely cultivated white grape variety of France and the mainstay of many a cheap dry white wine. To date it has been better known as the provider of base wine for distilling into armagnac and cognac, but lately the name has been appearing on wine labels. Technology seems to be improving the performance of the grape. The curious name is pronounced 'OON-yee', and is the same variety as Italy's ubiquitous Trebbiano.

Utiel-Requena – Region and *Denominación de Origen* of Mediterranean Spain inland from Valencia. Principally red wines from Bobal, Garnacha and Tempranillo grapes grown at relatively high altitude, between 600 and 900 metres.

V

Vacqueyras – Village of the southern Rhône Valley of France in the region better known for its generic appellation, the Côtes du Rhône. Vacqueyras can date its winemaking history all the way back to 1414, but has only been producing under its own village AC since 1991. The wines, from Grenache and Syrah grapes, can be wonderfully silky and intense, spicy and long-lived.

Valdepeñas – An island of quality production amidst the ocean of mediocrity that is Spain's La Mancha region – where most of the grapes are grown for distilling into the head-banging brandies of Jerez. Valdepeñas reds are made from a grape they call the Cencibel – which turns out to be a very close relation of the Tempranillo grape that is the mainstay of the fine but expensive red wines of Rioja. Again, like Rioja, Valdepeñas wines are matured in oak casks to give them a vanilla-rich smoothness. Among bargain reds, Valdepeñas is a name to look out for.

Valpolicella – Red wine of Verona, Italy. Good examples have ripe, cherry fruit and a pleasingly dry finish. Unfortunately, there are many bad examples of Valpolicella. Shop with circumspection. Valpolicella Classico wines, from the best vineyards clustered around the town, are more reliable. Those additionally labelled *superiore* have higher alcohol and some bottle age.

vanilla – Ageing wines in oak barrels (or, less picturesquely, adding oak chips to wine in huge concrete vats) imparts a range of characteristics including a smell of vanilla from the ethyl vanilline naturally given off by oak.

varietal – A varietal wine is one named after the grape variety (one or more) from which it is made. Nearly all everyday wines worldwide are now labelled in this way. It is salutary to contemplate that until the present wine boom began in the 1980s, wines described thus were virtually unknown outside Germany and one or two quirky regions of France and Italy.

vegan-friendly – My informal way of noting that a wine is claimed to have been made not only with animal-product-free finings (*see* vegetarian wine) but without any animal-related products whatsoever, such as manure in the vineyards.

vegetal – A tasting note definitely open to interpretation. It suggests a smell or flavour reminiscent less of fruit (apple, pineapple, strawberry and the like) than of something leafy or even root based. Some wines are evocative (to some tastes) of beetroot, cabbage or even unlikelier vegetable flavours – and these characteristics may add materially to the attraction of the wine.

vegetarian wine – Wines labelled 'suitable for vegetarians' have been made without the assistance of animal products for 'fining' – clarifying – before bottling. Gelatine, egg whites, isinglass from fish bladders and casein from milk are among the items shunned, usually in favour of bentonite, an absorbent clay first found at Benton in the US state of Montana.

Verdejo – White grape of the Rueda region in north-west Spain. It can make superbly perfumed crisp dry whites of truly distinctive character and has helped make Rueda one of the best white-wine sources of Europe. No relation to Verdelho.

Verdelho – Portuguese grape variety once mainly used for a medium-dry style of Madeira, also called Verdelho, but now rare. The vine is now prospering in Australia, where it can make well-balanced dry whites with fleeting richness and lemon-lime acidity.

Verdicchio – White grape variety of Italy best known in the DOC zone of Castelli di Jesi in the Adriatic wine region of the Marches. Dry white wines once known for little more than their naff amphora-style bottles but now gaining a reputation for interesting, herbaceous flavours of recognisable character.

Vermentino – White grape variety principally of Italy, especially Sardinia. Makes florally scented soft dry whites.

Vieilles vignes – Old vines. Many French producers like to claim on their labels that the wine within is from vines of notable antiquity. While it's true that vines don't produce useful grapes for the first few years after planting, it is uncertain whether vines of much greater age – say 25 years plus – than others actually make better fruit. There are no regulations governing the use of the term, so it's not a reliable indicator anyway.

Vin de France – In effect, the new Vin de Table of France's morphing wine laws. The term Vin de Table has just about disappeared – or should have, under new legislation introduced in 2010 – and Vin de France installed as the designation of a wine guaranteed to have been produced in France. The label may state the vintage (if all the wine in the blend does come from a single year's harvest) and the grape varieties that constitute the wine. It may not state the region of France from which the wine comes.

vin de liqueur – Sweet style of white wine mostly from the Pyrenean region of south-westernmost France, made by adding a little spirit to the new wine before it has fermented out, halting the fermentation and retaining sugar.

vin de pays – 'Country wine' of France. The French map is divided up into more than 100 vin de pays regions. Introduced in 1968 and regularly revised ever since, it's the wine-quality designation between basic Vin de France and AOC/AOP. Although being superseded by the more recently introduced IGP (*qv*), there are more than 150 producing areas permitted to use the description vin de pays. Some vin de pays areas are huge: the Vin de Pays d'Oc (named after the Languedoc region) covers much of the Midi and Provence. Plenty of wines bearing this humble designation are of astoundingly high quality and certainly compete with New World counterparts for interest and value. *See* Indication Géographique Protégée.

vin de table – Formerly official designation of generic French wine, now used only informally. *See* Vin de France.

vin doux naturel – Sweet, mildly fortified wine of southern France. A little spirit is added during the winemaking process, halting the fermentation by killing the yeast before it has consumed all the sugars – hence the pronounced sweetness of the wine.

vin gris – Rosé wine from Provence.

Vinho de mesa – 'Table wine' of Portugal.

Vino da tavola – The humblest official classification of Italian wine. Much ordinary plonk bears this designation, but the bizarre quirks of Italy's wine laws dictate that some of that country's finest wines are also classed as mere vino da tavola (table wine). If an expensive Italian wine is labelled as such, it doesn't mean it will be a disappointment.

Vino de mesa – 'Table wine' of Spain. Usually very ordinary.

vintage – The grape harvest. The year displayed on bottle labels is the year of the harvest. Wines bearing no date have been blended from the harvests of two or more years.

Viognier – A grape variety once exclusive to the northern Rhône Valley in France where it makes a very chi-chi wine, Condrieu, usually costing £20 plus. Now, the Viognier is grown more widely, in North and South America as well as elsewhere in France, and occasionally produces soft, marrowy whites that echo the grand style of Condrieu itself. The Viognier is now commonly blended with Shiraz in red winemaking in Australia and South Africa. It does not dilute the colour and is confidently believed by highly experienced winemakers to enhance the quality. Steve Webber, in charge of winemaking at the revered De Bortoli estates in the Yarra Valley region of Victoria, Australia, puts between two and five per cent Viognier in with some of his Shiraz wines. 'I think it's the perfume,' he told me. 'It gives some femininity to the wine.'

Viura – White grape variety of Rioja, Spain. Also widely grown elsewhere in Spain under the name Macabeo. Wines have a blossomy aroma and are dry, but sometimes soft at the expense of acidity.

Vouvray – AC of the Loire Valley, France, known for still and sparkling dry white wines and sweet, still whites from late-harvested grapes. The wines, all from Chenin Blanc grapes, have a unique capacity for unctuous softness combined with lively freshness – an effect best portrayed in the demi-sec (slightly sweet) wines, which can be delicious and keenly priced. Unfashionable, but worth looking out for.

Vranac – Black grape variety of the Balkans known for dense colour and tangy-bitter edge to the flavour. Best enjoyed in situ.

W

weight – In an ideal world the weight of a wine is determined by the ripeness of the grapes from which it has been made. In some cases the weight is determined merely by the quantity of sugar added during the production process. A good, genuine wine described as having weight is one in which there is plenty of alcohol and 'extract' – colour and flavour from the grapes. Wine enthusiasts judge weight by swirling the wine in the glass and then examining the 'legs' or 'tears' left clinging to the inside of the glass after the contents have subsided. Alcohol gives these runlets a dense, glycerine-like condition, and if they cling for a long time, the wine is deemed to have weight – a very good thing in all honestly made wines.

Winzergenossenschaft – One of the many very lengthy and peculiar words regularly found on labels of German wines. This means a winemaking co-operative. Many excellent German wines are made by these associations of growers.

woodsap – A subjective tasting note. Some wines have a fleeting bitterness, which is not a fault, but an interesting balancing factor amidst very ripe flavours. The effect somehow evokes woodsap.

X

Xarel-lo – One of the main grape varieties for cava, the sparkling wine of Spain.

Xinomavro – Black grape variety of Greece. It retains its acidity even in the very hot conditions that prevail in many Greek vineyards, where harvests tend to over-ripen and make cooked-tasting wines. Modern winemaking techniques are capable of making well-balanced wines from Xinomavro.

Y

Yecla – Town and DO wine region of eastern Spain, close to Alicante, making lots of interesting, strong-flavoured red and white wines, often at bargain prices.

yellow – White wines are not white at all, but various shades of yellow – or, more poetically, gold. Some white wines with opulent richness even have a flavour I cannot resist calling yellow – reminiscent of butter.

Z

Zibibbo – Sicilian white grape variety synonymous with north African variety Muscat of Alexandria. Scantily employed in sweet winemaking, and occasionally for drier styles.

Zinfandel – Black grape variety of California. Makes brambly reds, some of which can age very gracefully, and 'blush' whites – actually pink, because a little of the skin colour is allowed to leach into the must. The vine is also planted in Australia and South America. The Primitivo of southern Italy is said to be a related variety, but makes a very different kind of wine.